DESIGN
AND CATASTROPHE

DESIGN
AND CATASTROPHE

51 SCIENTISTS EXPLORE EVIDENCE IN NATURE

Edited by
**L. James Gibson
Ronny Nalin
Humberto M. Rasi**

Andrews
University Press
Berrien Springs, Michigan

Andrews University Press
Sutherland House
8360 W. Campus Circle Dr.
Berrien Springs, MI 49104–1700
Telephone: 269–471–6134; Fax: 269–471–6224
Email: aupo@andrews.edu
Website: https://universitypress.andrews.edu

ISBN: 978-1-940980-30-0

Printed in the United States of America
25 24 23 22 21   1 2 3 4 5

All Scripture quotations, unless otherwise indicated, are taken from the Holy Bible, New International Version®, NIV®. Copyright ©1973, 1978, 1984, 2011 by Biblica, Inc.™ Used by permission of Zondervan. All rights reserved worldwide. www.zondervan.com. The "NIV" and "New International Version" are trademarks registered in the United States Patent and Trademark Office by Biblica, Inc.™

Library of Congress Cataloging-in-Publication Data

Names: Gibson, L. James, editor. | Nalin, Ronny, editor. | Rasi, H. M.
   (Humberto M.), editor.
Title: Design and catastrophe : 51 scientists explore evidence in nature /
   edited by L. James Gibson, Ronny Nalin, and Humberto M. Rasi.
Description: Berrien Springs, Michigan : Andrews University Press, [2021] |
   Includes bibliographical references. | Summary: "An in-depth exploration
   of the way the biblical record illuminates various phenomena observed in
   the natural world"-- Provided by publisher.
Identifiers: LCCN 2020040585 | ISBN 9781940980300 (hardback)
Subjects: LCSH: Intelligent design (Teleology)
Classification: LCC BS651 .D475 2021 | DDC 231.7/652--dc23
LC record available at https://lccn.loc.gov/2020040585

Project Director	Ronald Alan Knott
Project Editor	Deborah L. Everhart
Copy Editing	Jan Levin
Editorial Assistance	Jasmine Logan, Paige J. Swanson
Cover Design	Robert N. Mason
Imagery Artwork	Uriel Lemuel Garcia Millán
Typesetting	Federico Richter
Proofreading	Rebecca Faith

Typeset: 10.5/14 Minion Pro

CONTENTS

PART III ● A Green World   59

PART IV ● Filling the Waters and the Air   71

PART V ● Let the Earth Bring Forth   91

PART VI ● In God's Image   105

PART VII ● Interdependence and Cooperation 125

PART VIII ● Out of Eden 139

PART IX ● Vestiges of Catastrophe 155

CONCLUSION ● 187

INTRODUCTION

Our world is replete with examples of design and catastrophe, two universal features of the natural world. We define "design" as the purposeful arrangement of parts for a function, reflecting intelligent planning rather than chance and necessity. In this context, "catastrophe" means the collapse or destruction of a functional system at a rate faster than the background of ordinary events. This book presents several and varied examples of both design and catastrophe, drawn from the rich experience of expert scientists. These examples serve to remind us that faith and science can interact in productive ways.

Our purpose in presenting the examples of design and catastrophe discussed here is to illustrate how we may use the perspective of the biblical record to help us understand our world. In a broad sense, the design we see in nature reflects the Creation story described in Genesis 1 and 2. Likewise, in a broader sense, much of the evidence of catastrophe we see in nature adds to our conception of the global event described in Genesis 7 and 8.

The biblical stories of Creation, the Fall, redemption, and restoration are grounded in the first chapters of Genesis. Therefore, we are not surprised to see evidence of design and catastrophe in nature. If these were unobservable, we would wonder why. The biblical explanation of Creation and the Flood interfaces with the scientific discoveries of design and catastrophe and encourages us to study science and Scripture more deeply. As a result, we expect to expand our understanding of God's activities in the world He created and sustains.

The scientists who have contributed to this book have found in their experience that the biblical perspective illuminates what we see in nature. Where questions remain, and there are many, we see them as opportunities for learning. We do not propose that the examples of design and catastrophe discussed here should be used to claim proof of the biblical record. They do not and cannot. Rather, the Bible provides an explanation as to why we observe these features.

The contributors represent a broad diversity of topical expertise—from cosmology to chemistry and particle physics, from ecology to molecular biology, and also in medicine and engineering. All authors have earned doctorates, mostly PhD or equivalent.

The book is organized in a unique way. The various topics are not arranged by discipline, as is typically the case. Instead, they are arranged in a sequence that is intended to loosely parallel the sequence of historical events recorded in the first several chapters of Genesis. Accordingly, the first chapters of this book describe the design seen in the universe regarding the laws governing the structure and interactions of matter and some aspects of the inorganic parts of our world. These topics correspond to the first several verses of Genesis 1.

The book moves to the subject of life and its origin, the design seen at the biomolecular level, and then, more specifically, to the design in plants and the process of photosynthesis, representing the third day of creation. From there we move to the inhabitants of the waters and air, correlating with the fifth day of Creation. The sixth day of Creation deals with the design of land animals, especially humans. The following chapters illustrate how design is seen in ecological relationships, interconnectedness, and cooperation, reflecting the assessment that the completed Creation was "very good."

Next, the context shifts from the "very good" assessment to the fallen world and the changes that occurred as a result. Animals were designed to be able to adapt to the changing environment. Nevertheless, many species were destroyed in a global catastrophe. That catastrophe changed the surface of the earth, produced immense deposits of sediments and other geological features, and had lasting effects on life on the planet.

Although Scripture provides much helpful information, there remain many unanswered questions, and this book includes some suggestions regarding how to continue the pursuit of seeking a better understanding. The final chapter ends on a more personal note, showing how design, catastrophe, and the hope of restoration can become very tangible components of our life. For the writers of this book, the Bible provides a useful and reliable guide for interpreting the evidence we see in Creation. It is our hope that the testimony of design and catastrophe will encourage the reader to join in the pursuit of using the light of Scripture to gain a better understanding of our world, its history, and its Creator.

The editors express their appreciation to the Department of Education of the General Conference of Seventh-day Adventists and to the Foundation for Adventist Education for the financial support that has facilitated the publication of this book. We also wish to acknowledge the capable editorial assistance of Katherine Ching.

Ronny Nalin and Humberto Rasi are pleased to dedicate their participation in this project in honor of the lifelong service in the arena of faith and science of their colleague and co-editor of this volume, Dr. Jim Gibson. His perspective on design and catastrophe as the two major lenses for the study of nature is reflected in the underlying purpose of this book.

The Editors

PART I

In the Beginning

The Fine-Tuning of the Universe

Aleksei Popov

When we look up at the starry sky in a cloudless night, we admire the beauty of the picture that opens before our eyes. Countless stars, star clusters, nebulae, and galaxies capture our imagination and raise the question, What caused all this to exist? Is it natural that our universe contains such complex (and beautiful) structures? Since the structure of the universe is regulated by natural laws, a second question could be raised that is closely related to the first: Why do these laws act in such a way that all of these complex structures can exist? The "strength" of the laws of physics is determined by the relatively small number of so-called "fundamental constants," such as the gravitational constant, the speed of light, Planck's constant, the mass of the electron, and so on. The word "fundamental" means that these constants cannot be derived from any other laws; their numerical values are "given from above," and we can only measure them experimentally.

For a long time, scientists assumed that the structure of the universe is stable to the variation of these constants. This situation started to change in the first half of the twentieth century when several scientists, such as Paul Dirac, proposed that fundamental constants may change over long periods of time.[1] This proposal triggered intensive study of the potential stability of the universe in the face of possible changes in the fundamental constants. The result of the study, which was unexpected for many scientists, was that our universe is very unstable to such variations. The numerical values of these fundamental constants are fine-tuned to provide the complex structure of the universe that we see. If these constants were to deviate from the measured values, all complex structures in the universe would cease to exist. Following are some examples that demonstrate this statement.

Masses of the Proton and Neutron

These masses are very close to each other with differences between them being 1,000 times smaller than the masses themselves, but making possible the existence of all chemical elements in the universe. If the mass of a neutron were just 1% higher than its actual value, neutrons inside the atomic nuclei of most chemical elements would be unstable. These elements simply could not exist. The same would be true if the mass of a proton were a little smaller than its present value. Conversely, if the mass of a proton were just 0.2% higher than its present value, protons would be unstable and the existence of hydrogen, which is a main constituent component of stars, would be impossible. The same is true for the mass of a neutron—if it were just 0.2% less than its actual value, it would lead to proton instability with dramatic consequences for our universe.

The Constant of the Strong Interactions

The strong interaction is a force that holds protons and neutrons inside the atomic nuclei. If this force (the value of which is determined by the strong interaction constant) were just 5% smaller, it would lead (among other destructive consequences) to the absence of deuterium in our universe. Without deuterium, the proton-proton nuclear reaction—a base reaction in the sequence of nuclear reactions inside the stars—would not proceed, which would lead to a starless universe. If the strong interaction constant were just 2% bigger, it would lead to the existence of a "di-proton" (the bound state of two protons). With the existence of di-protons, the speed of the proton-proton reaction would be 10^{18} times faster, and stars would burn out completely during a very short period of time, also leading to a starless universe.[2]

Relationship between Gravitational and Electromagnetic Interactions

Gravity is responsible for the force of attraction between all massive bodies in the universe and defines the structure of the universe at large scales. The electromagnetic force is responsible (among other things) for the attractive/repulsive force between electrical charges. An unexpected fact is that the electromagnetic force is 10^{40} times higher than the force of gravity. Two equally charged massive bodies repel each other $\sim 10^{40}$ more strongly by the electric force than attract by the force of gravity. The ratio between the gravitational and electromagnetic forces (10^{-40}) is tiny but plays a very important part in the life of stars. If this ratio (which is already very small) were slightly less, all stars would be red dwarfs. If it were just slightly bigger, all stars would be blue giants. In either case, just a small deviation from this number would lead to the absence of Sun-like stars in the universe.[3]

Conclusions

We have considered only three examples of fine-tuning in the universe, but there are many more such examples. The very important questions that emerge are, Who did this? Who (or what) is responsible for this fine-tuning? Who (or what) put all of the fundamental constants in their places? In general, there are only two possible answers to those questions: they were given exactly the right values by chance, or by purpose. If the former is true, we can estimate the probability of such a fine-tuning event occurring just by chance. And if we calculate this probability, it will look really improbable—there are several estimates that vary from $10^{-3,000}$ to $10^{-10^{123}}$![4,5] Both of these numbers are indescribably small and simply mean "nothing," or "impossible." Modern attempts to overcome this huge improbability by the so-called "multiverse" (many universes) theories should face the facts of non-observability of the other "universes" and non-falsifiability of such theories. And, in the end, we have to return to the first verse of the Bible: "In the beginning God created the heavens and the earth."

2

Where Does Matter Come From?

Alfredo Takashi Suzuki

Merriam-Webster's online dictionary defines the noun "design" as "deliberate purposive planning."[1] The qualifications "deliberate" and "purposive" imply the existence of some kind of volition behind the action of planning. Designing demands a priori, the foreseeing of an Intelligence capable of deliberate actions and purposes.

Consider the following hypothetical situation in which someone wants to build an electric toaster factory. Besides having to build the plant with appropriate machinery, find the right raw materials, and define the specifications of the industrial manufacturing process, he or she also needs to understand the basics of energy transformation in order to produce ovens that will operate in an efficient and safe way. Any expected function or specification, such as the color of the toasters, has to be addressed beforehand, for example, by adding a step to apply a coating of the right color somewhere along the production line. Clearly, "deliberate, purposive planning" is required for the designing of toasters.

Everywhere we look in nature, we can see evidence for this kind of design. However, when it comes to natural systems, some contend that what we observe is only an illusion or appearance of purposeful design.[2] What, then, is the true origin of our world?

Let us do some thought experimentation to address this question, since in historical science one cannot perform actual experiments. For the sake of argumentation, pretend that our system to analyze is the entire universe, at an original stage with no matter or energy—a total vacuum—and with no space or time structured in it. And from this, the entire universe we see today arose. Everything we have today came from nothing. That is the essence of the big bang proposition. Since there is no natural mechanism that can explain this "nothing-to-everything" process, we cannot even label it as scientific hypothesis. It takes a gigantic leap of faith to believe in such a(n) (im)possibility.

Next, let us concede a different initial system with which to begin: Let our universe be without matter but with lots of pure energy, as much as required for anything, whether transforming into different forms, doing some work, or "materializing." What kind of energy could that possibly be? It cannot be potential or nuclear or any of the forms that need matter to produce or store. The only possibility would be electromagnetic energy. However, classically, electromagnetic radiation is produced by oscillating electric charges, which, by assumption, we do not have yet. Quantically, there are two possibilities: radiation from an atomic electron's excited state transitioning to lower energy states (which is also not yet possible, since we are assuming there are no atoms yet), or the quantum field "vacuum," populated by zero-point quantum harmonic oscillator energies.

Admitting that some fortuitous quantum fluctuations might happen in this vacuum to produce electron-positron[3] and proton-antiproton pairs according to the famous Einstein's equation $E = mc^2$, and that these protons are attracted electromagnetically to the electrons, then, in principle we have a mechanism whereby hydrogen atoms might have been produced. But the issue is not so much about the possible mechanisms for the production of matter, as important as they may be. The real issue is that hydrogen atoms need precise specifications to have all the properties that allow for all the chemical combinations with other atoms, specifications such as the appropriate mass, charge, and spin for the proton and electron, and their right dimensions (size) and distance between each other. Properties, functionality, and appearance for these particles that compose the atom all must be determined before its creation.

There are a couple of other problems with this suggested mechanism of pair production for the primordial nucleosynthesis.

To begin with, it is only when energetic radiation interacts with matter that pair production can occur, but in our assumption there is no matter yet with which to interact. And without this interaction, simple pair production in space is forbidden, because it would violate momentum conservation, a fundamental tenet in physics.[4] Moreover, for each electron (matter) that is produced, one positron (antimatter) is produced at the same time, and the same is true of the proton-antiproton pair. The antiproton and positron would form an anti-hydrogen, which would immediately annihilate hydrogen upon collision, returning matter again to pure energy. But, the universe as we see it is full of matter alone, so there is an essential asymmetry in relation to anti-matter.[5] Having all the correct specifications for the hydrogen atom (and, by extension, for all matter in the universe), this matter asymmetry requires the volition of a superior Mind that, with deliberate, purposive planning, designed matter as we know it in the universe, with all its correct properties.

To imagine that in the beginning of the universe we had only quantum field "vacuum" energy from which fortuitous quantum fluctuations gave rise to pair productions in the nucleosynthesis simply does not hold to an honest scrutiny of modern scientific knowledge.

Atoms, as we know them in nature, bear within themselves the clear fingerprints of design, pointing to a Designer with superior intellect and volition, or, as the Scriptures beautifully declare, "In the beginning ..." *Logos* (John 1:1).

3

The Periodic Table and Design

Nicholas Madhiri

The periodic table of elements is one of the most fascinating features in the physical sciences. It consists of the arrangement of elements in a well-organized, repeating pattern, hence the term "periodic." All materials in the universe are made up of elements represented on the periodic table, and these elements seem to tell a consistently elegant story about the organization and function of matter at its fundamental level.

We may ask, "Where did all these elements come from and why can they be arranged in such a well-organized, predictable order?" The standard naturalistic model argues that the elements formed as a result of a non-directed, big explosion billions of years ago, called the big bang.[1] However, looking at the periodic table (Figure 3-1), one wonders how such a massive explosion could produce such a well-ordered, beautiful pattern. There are features that seem to point to an Intelligence behind nature as reflected in the periodic table of elements.

Elements differ by the number of protons, subatomic particles in the nucleus of each atom. If the elements are arranged in order of the number of protons, they form a continuous numerical pattern.

The periodic table reveals a periodicity of the elements, whereby in each period (its row on the periodic table), there is a progression of chemical and physical properties from the first column to a climax in the last column before the pattern is repeated. For example, element numbers 2, 10, 18, 36, and so on, become climactic points, after which the periodic cycle begins again.

Legend:

26	atomic number
Fe	chemical symbol
iron	name
55.845	standard atomic weight

1	2	3	4	5	6	7	8	9	10	11	12	13	14	15	16	17	18
H 1 hydrogen 1.0079																	**He** 2 helium 4.0026
Li 3 lithium 6.941	**Be** 4 beryllium 9.0122											**B** 5 boron 10.811	**C** 6 carbon 12.011	**N** 7 nitrogen 14.007	**O** 8 oxygen 15.999	**F** 9 fluorine 18.998	**Ne** 10 neon 20.180
Na 11 sodium 22.990	**Mg** 12 magnesium 24.305											**Al** 13 aluminum 26.982	**Si** 14 silicon 28.086	**P** 15 phosphorus 30.974	**S** 16 sulfur 32.065	**Cl** 17 chlorine 35.453	**Ar** 18 argon 39.948
K 19 potassium 39.098	**Ca** 20 calcium 40.078	**Sc** 21 scandium 44.956	**Ti** 22 titanium 47.867	**V** 23 vanadium 50.942	**Cr** 24 chromium 51.996	**Mn** 25 manganese 54.938	**Fe** 26 iron 55.845	**Co** 27 cobalt 58.933	**Ni** 28 nickel 58.693	**Cu** 29 copper 63.546	**Zn** 30 zinc 65.38	**Ga** 31 gallium 69.723	**Ge** 32 germanium 72.64	**As** 33 arsenic 74.922	**Se** 34 selenium 78.96	**Br** 35 bromine 79.904	**Kr** 36 krypton 83.798
Rb 37 rubidium 85.468	**Sr** 38 strontium 87.62	**Y** 39 yttrium 88.906	**Zr** 40 zirconium 91.224	**Nb** 41 niobium 92.906	**Mo** 42 molybdenum 95.96	**Tc** 43 technetium [98]	**Ru** 44 ruthenium 101.07	**Rh** 45 rhodium 102.91	**Pd** 46 palladium 106.42	**Ag** 47 silver 107.87	**Cd** 48 cadmium 112.41	**In** 49 indium 114.82	**Sn** 50 tin 118.71	**Sb** 51 antimony 121.76	**Te** 52 tellurium 127.60	**I** 53 iodine 126.90	**Xe** 54 xenon 131.29
Cs 55 caesium 132.91	**Ba** 56 barium 137.33		**Hf** 72 hafnium 178.49	**Ta** 73 tantalum 180.95	**W** 74 tungsten 183.84	**Re** 75 rhenium 186.21	**Os** 76 osmium 190.23	**Ir** 77 iridium 192.22	**Pt** 78 platinum 195.08	**Au** 79 gold 196.97	**Hg** 80 mercury 200.59	**Tl** 81 thallium 204.38	**Pb** 82 lead 207.2	**Bi** 83 bismuth 208.98	**Po** 84 polonium [209]	**At** 85 astatine [210]	**Rn** 86 radon [222]
Fr 87 francium [223]	**Ra** 88 radium [226]		**Rf** 104 rutherfordium [261]	**Db** 105 dubnium [262]	**Sg** 106 seaborgium [266]	**Bh** 107 bohrium [264]	**Hs** 108 hassium [277]	**Mt** 109 meitnerium [268]	**Ds** 110 darmstadtium [271]	**Rg** 111 roentgenium [272]							

La 57 lanthanum 138.91	**Ce** 58 cerium 140.12	**Pr** 59 praseodymium 140.91	**Nd** 60 neodymium 144.24	**Pm** 61 promethium [145]	**Sm** 62 samarium 150.36	**Eu** 63 europium 151.96	**Gd** 64 gadolinium 157.25	**Tb** 65 terbium 158.93	**Dy** 66 dysprosium 162.50	**Ho** 67 holmium 164.93	**Er** 68 erbium 167.26	**Tm** 69 thulium 168.93	**Yb** 70 ytterbium 173.05	**Lu** 71 lutetium 174.97
Ac 89 actinium [227]	**Th** 90 thorium 232.04	**Pa** 91 protactinium 231.04	**U** 92 uranium 238.03	**Np** 93 neptunium [237]	**Pu** 94 plutonium [244]	**Am** 95 americium [243]	**Cm** 96 curium [247]	**Bk** 97 berkelium [247]	**Cf** 98 californium [251]	**Es** 99 einsteinium [252]	**Fm** 100 fermium [257]	**Md** 101 mendelevium [258]	**No** 102 nobelium [259]	**Lr** 103 lawrencium [262]

FIGURE 3-1. The periodic table of elements. The number on the top right corner of each element is the number of protons (atomic number). The simplest element is Hydrogen (H), and it has one proton. For successive elements, the number of protons is counting and continuous.

Moving across each period, the atomic radius of each successive element gets smaller and smaller before the cycle repeats itself. In each period, atoms in the first column are always the largest, while elements in the last column are the smallest.

Atoms also contain the same number of electrons as protons. These particles stabilize each other, although they do not reside in the same part of the atom. Protons reside in the nucleus (center of the atom), while electrons reside in the peripheral regions of the atom. Moreover, electrons are not randomly scattered around the atom but reside in certain specific levels, with each level only allowing a specific number of residing electrons. Electrons interact with each other, some arrangements and interactions being more favorable than others.

Elements in the same column have the same number of electrons in the outermost level and tend to have similar chemical properties. For example, all elements in the first column have one electron in their outermost level and react violently with water, which generates hydrogen and a tremendous amount of heat that can ignite the hydrogen, generating fire.[2] On the other hand, all elements in the last column tend to be very unreactive and seldom bond together to form complex molecules.

Such arrangements of electrons also allow chemical combinations to occur in specific, predictable manners. Scientists are able to predict which elements will react with which, and how. For example, the chemical formula for water is H_2O. This means that regardless of the source and how it is prepared, water will always have a 2:1 ratio between hydrogen and oxygen. It is this predictability that has allowed the study of chemistry to be such a useful and rewarding enterprise. Commenting on this amazing proportionality, Poythress remarked that "chemists discovered the elegant proportionality of chemical bonding even before we had a conception of atomic structure."[3]

A third subatomic particle, the neutron, also plays a stabilizing role to the nucleus through the strong nuclear force. Without neutrons, the heavier elements would not form due to massive repulsive forces between protons. It almost seems like foresight was involved to make the necessary particles needed for the atom to exist ahead of time.

Although scientists do not agree on the origin of the elements and these subatomic particles, the periodic properties of these elements seem to communicate a directed process. Any directed process, however, requires a built-in code or set of instructions. The question is, If the process of formation of these elements is purely natural, then what is the nature and source of this coding system?

How can such beautiful construction of order even at subatomic and fundamental levels be random and undirected? Beauty, order, and predictability, especially in complex systems, testify of an Intelligence behind their construction. The atom, though small, is so complex that it determines the nature, structure, and strength of large objects and organisms. To observe that at a fundamental level matter exhibits such modularity and predictable interactions is, to me, indicative of design rather than chance.

In conclusion, although an exhaustive study of the periodic table is beyond the scope of this essay, the few trends highlighted communicate a beautiful, orderly pattern that contradicts the narrative of a random, non-directed natural process of origination. This order and design are revealed on many levels of the atomic structure and affect the configuration and properties of all materials in this universe. For me, the most reasonable conclusion is that behind the intricate design of the atom there must be a masterful, careful, and purposeful Designer—the Creator God.

4

The Heavens Declare God's Glory

Mart de Groot

At age eighteen I went to study astronomy at a university with the motto *"Sol Iustitiae Illustra Nos"* (Sun of Righteousness, shine upon us). A couple of years later this struck a chord and I accepted Christ as my Savior, adopting Psalm 19:1 as my favorite Bible verse: "The heavens declare the glory of God; the skies proclaim the work of his hands." I started looking for relations between science and religion. This is what I found: when I learn about a character trait of God, I find it reflected in an astronomical situation or event; and, vice versa, many astronomical events or configurations point me to some character trait of God.

God Loves People

When I read Genesis 1, I often stand amazed at the brevity of the account of how the transformation of Earth from utter chaos into a habitable planet happened in just six days. Even more amazing, the origin of the cosmos, the extraterrestrial part of our immense universe, is announced in just thirty-nine words that are not part of the description of the six days. This creates the impression, not coincidental I believe, that Earth's habitat and the creatures that live here are more important to God than the rest of creation. God loves the people created in His image.

Catastrophes

One only needs to read a few more pages in Genesis to find out that humans' distrust of God's love resulted in the Fall and the curse on creation. From that day forward, apart from moral and spiritual catastrophes, we read also about physical catastrophes with an apparently cosmic origin: the Flood in Noah's days (water from heaven and from the depths of the earth, Gen. 6–8), and the destruction of Sodom and Gomorrah (fire from heaven, Gen. 19), among others. The moral catastrophe of the Fall is reflected in nature's disasters.

I will define a catastrophic event in the cosmos as a seemingly natural event causing loss of life and/or property on Earth. High-energy events in remote places that do no damage on Earth are not called catastrophes. I suggest that we should enjoy these as interesting phenomena that invite us to investigate further, to learn more about the behavior of matter in extreme conditions, as well as to learn about the Creator Himself.

God's almighty power is shown in stellar outbursts beyond the solar system. A supernova can be as powerful as 1,000 kilonovae, each of which can be as powerful as 1,000 novae. Topping it all are gigantic outbursts, gamma ray bursts: although they last less than a second, they emit as much energy as the sun emits in one million years, with the potential of sterilizing any planet in their neighborhood and killing all life that might exist there.

While we may find comfort in the remoteness of Earth from these events, we must realize that our sun is an active star producing serious outbursts from time to time. Solar flares and coronal mass ejections fire streams of high-energy particles and radiation toward Earth. Major outbursts can disturb the electric grid, communication systems, Earth's satellites (and the Global Positioning System, among other things), and air travel. Because of current society's dependence on high tech, relatively minor disturbances can have serious consequences. However, major outbursts are relatively rare, and the more frequent, smaller outbursts do not do much harm. Science is also finding ever-better methods of forecasting solar weather, as the impact of the sun's activity on Earth is now called.

Design

My early university years also marked the beginning of the space age, when the Russian Sputnik 2 carried a living being—Laika, the dog—into space. Since the Bible hints at the presence of other intelligent creatures in the universe (Neh. 9:6; Job 1:6; 38:7), the search for life on extrasolar planets (also called exoplanets) was on. On April 18, 2019, the number of confirmed exoplanets stood at 3,944.[1] In the face of the hazards described above, one wonders what chances life will have for existing on these planets. And, though red dwarfs—stars with less than half the sun's mass—are the most numerous candidates for central stars of exoplanetary systems, their outbursts are far more energetic than our sun's, making life around them almost impossible.

Earth's location near a less active star, our sun, far away from the lethal ionizing radiation near the center of the Milky Way, with conditions—water in its three phases; an atmosphere protecting us from heavy bombardment by meteorites, comets, and asteroids; and conditions just right for photosynthesis—in perfect tune with the necessities of life, testify of an intelligent Designer whose primary objective is clearly the well-being of His many varied creatures.

Furthermore, the fundamental forces of nature (e.g., gravity, electromagnetism, nuclear forces) are fine-tuned, in many instances within extremely narrow margins, such that when just one parameter is out of tune, life cannot be sustained. Habitability is an exacting demand. The Bible points us to these character traits of God as order, omniscience, and planning.

Finally, Earth's location in the cosmos and its position as a stable observing platform from which we can investigate the rest of the universe challenge us to investigate the universe and learn more about God's character (Ps. 19:1). The knowledge of God and His character helps lead to eternal life (John 17:3). Whoever wants to study the universe will find in God a wise Guide who knows every detail of His grand Creation and who is willing to put us on the right track before we endeavor to investigate the universe (Isa. 40:26).

Conclusion

The Christian who looks at the Bible's Creation report can find assurance that our Creator is in control of everything that happens in the universe when He announces at the end of Creation week that everything "was very good" (Gen. 1:31). In this view, the presence of catastrophic events, though scary, can be understood if we remember God's foresight and promise—foresight of our moral failure resulting in the curse upon Creation, and promise of His plan to restore creation to its original glory (Gen. 3:16–19; Rom. 8:20–22; Rev. 21:5). Thus, catastrophes remind us of our faults, and design helps us to look forward to new heavens and a new earth, where righteousness dwells and harmony is beyond our wildest dreams (Isa. 65:17; 1 Cor. 2:9; 2 Peter 3:13).

5

Wonderful Water

Rafael Schäffer

Water is vital for life. In the search for extraterrestrial life, the absence of water is generally considered an exclusion criterion for life as we know it. However, for most people, water is nothing special. We use it daily for drinking, cooking, cleaning, and washing. We just have to open the faucet and it's readily available in abundance. H_2O is pretty simple stoichiometrically, but from a chemical and physical point of view, it is an extraordinary substance. This molecule possesses many of the fascinating and outstanding properties that are essential to life.

A water molecule consists of one atom of oxygen and two atoms of hydrogen. The bonding of the atoms takes place via their electrons and can be compared to a handshake: some people have a strong handshake, and some people a weak one. Similarly, various elements attract electrons to different degrees, creating bonds with different strengths. One measure of this attraction is called electronegativity. Oxygen has the second highest electronegativity, with a value of 3.4, whereas hydrogen has an average value of 2.2. To stay with the metaphor of the handshake, the oxygen atom pulls so hard that it attracts the two electrons of the hydrogen atoms. As a result, the oxygen atom is partially negatively charged, and the hydrogen atoms are partially positively charged. Opposing charges attract each other, therefore a three-dimensional network of hydrogen bonds forms between water molecules. This causes water to have many extraordinary and interesting properties, such as a relatively high melting and boiling point.

In the periodic table of the elements, oxygen is part of the chalcogens. The other chalcogens—sulfur (S), selenium (Se), tellurium (Te), and polonium (Po)—are relatives of oxygen. Among relatives, there are similarities and sometimes shared characteristics. So it is with chemical compounds. In fact, H_2S, H_2Se, H_2Te, and H_2Po have similar melting and boiling points. The melting points rise from -86 to -35°C, and the boiling points from -60 to 36°C. But water, at 0 and 100°C, does not fit into this pattern. Water should actually have significantly lower melting and boiling points. The reason for these relatively high temperatures is that a lot of energy has to be applied to break the hydrogen bonds. However, because of its melting point at 0°C and boiling point at 100°C, water is the only known substance that occurs in all three states of aggregation on Earth, and each state of aggregation fulfills essential functions on our planet.

Water vapor enables precipitation and the distribution of moisture over the planet. In addition, it causes ~60% of the natural greenhouse effect.[1] Without water vapor in the atmosphere, it would be 21°C colder on average,[2] making life possible only on a narrow strip along the equator, if at all. It is amazing to think that all these essential functions are accomplished by an evanescent vapor representing only 0.001% of the total budget of water on the earth.[3]

Ice also plays an important role in global climate regulation because of its high albedo—reflection of sunlight. Moreover, ice is an important drinking water reservoir. Usually, the solid phase of a substance is denser than the liquid phase. But the negative thermal expansion of waters allows ice to float on water, a phenomenon called density anomaly. This special feature is essential for aquatic life. Without this property, lakes, rivers, and seas would gradually freeze from bottom to top at negative temperatures, killing bottom dwellers and, if the whole water column froze, even swimming organisms.

Liquid water is the habitat for many plants and animals. It acts as a catalyst in many fundamental chemical reactions and can behave as both acid and base. Water is by far the most common component of the human body, its content varying according to age, gender, and physical condition, but being typically between 70% and 80% in adults. Water enables heat and mass transport on our planet because it is an excellent solvent and has by far the highest specific heat capacity of all liquids. The specific heat capacity is a measure of how much energy has to be applied to heat one gram of a substance by one degree. Just as electric energy can be stored and transported in a battery, so water stores and transports thermal energy between oceans and continents, the equator and the poles, summer and winter, day and night. Without this compensatory effect, there would be bigger and life-damaging temperature differences on Earth. Less than 2% of all water on Earth is groundwater and fresh water.[4] However, this seemingly negligible portion supplies almost all of humanity with drinking water.

There are a few more special features that make water extremely valuable for life, such as it having the second highest surface tension of all known liquids, the highest specific enthalpy of vaporization, as well as a low viscosity.

Finally, I would like to mention a property that often receives little attention in a scientific context: aesthetics. Ice crystals and snow crystals usually form in the highest symmetry of the hexagonal point symmetry group. The hexagonal axis gives the snow crystals their characteristic shape. Wilson Bentley (1865–1931) photographed more than 5,000 different snowflakes and in 1922 formulated the thesis: "No two snowflakes are alike." Under the microscope, there are similar or similar-looking crystals, but at the atomic level, every ice crystal is indeed unique.

In summary, ice, water, and steam have many remarkable properties. Without these qualities, life on Earth is hardly imaginable. Either these are huge coincidences and a happy interaction of different laws of nature, or an intelligent Being acted as engineer, coder, and designer and has projected, constructed, and programmed H_2O molecules genially and incomparably purposely. The latter possibility seems the more reasonable one, because it explains the observed water properties in the simplest and most elegant way.

6

From Chemical Space to Creative Grace

John C. Walton

Chemical space is an imaginary domain populated with examples of *all possible molecules*.[1] The number of different molecules that could be made by combining just a small set of 30 atoms in all possible ways comes to about 10^{24}, that is 10 followed by 24 zeros! This is roughly the same as the number of stars in the known universe. Of course, the total population of chemical space, from larger assemblages of atoms, is multiple orders of magnitude greater than this. Enzyme space and DNA space, which are subdomains of chemical space, are themselves stupendously large. The incredibly vast population of chemical space is the reason why finding new antibiotics is so difficult and why the growing resistance to drugs is such a serious problem. It is gradually dawning on the scientific community that exploration of this astronomical ocean of compounds is impossible, even computationally, in the supposed lifetime of planet Earth.[2]

No undirected evolutionary origin of life process, however efficient, would be able to find, in chemical space, just the relatively small set of molecules needed for a "simple" protocell, even in billions of years. The last few decades have revealed an astounding level of organized bio-complexity in one-celled microorganisms that was utterly unforeseen and unanticipated by Darwin or his successor evolutionists. Each cell actually contains many microscopic molecular machines that are composed of matched and ordered enzyme and nucleic acid networks. These are among the most complex things in the universe.

The hopelessness of evolutionary scenarios for the origin of living things is increasingly coming to light.

In contrast, Genesis offers a highly exalted view of God as a non-material and limitless Being transcending space and time. He is able to fashion and manipulate matter, molecules, and energy according to His designs and His timetable. He creates from nothing the earth and all its living inhabitants, whole, complete, and fully functioning, in a short period of time. His is a holistic Creation characterized by dynamic interconnections linking the living organisms to each other and to their material environment.

Cycles of mutual dependence and interrelationships are found everywhere in the natural world and are fundamental to its continuance. That they reach across so many diverse plant and animal groups and into the hydro- and ecospheres implies an overall design as well as a synchronized start-up. The origin of all living things must have been very rapid and coordinated, exactly as described in Genesis.

Many examples of the beneficial interrelationships between different organisms and between them and their physical environment can be cited. We humans need hundreds of other species to survive. We rely on stomach bacteria for digestive health. We need trees and plants in great variety to supply the oxygen we breathe. We can't eat soil, so we depend on lots of plants to extract essential components and supply them to us in tasty ways. All terrestrial life depends on lichens that help produce, during rock weathering, the soils from which plants obtain their nutrients. They live in partnership with green algae and fungi that supply food, minerals, nitrogen, and water. Plants utilize the carbon dioxide we breathe out as feedstock for their photosynthesis of carbohydrates. Legumes grow nodules on their roots containing nitrogen-fixing bacteria. They provide the bacteria with nutrients and food and, in return, the bacteria convert atmospheric nitrogen into ammonia that is essential for the plant's life. Eventually, plant nitrogen ends up as nitrates in the soil that fertilize more plant growth and development. Waste is virtually unknown in nature where recycling is the norm. The waste product excreted by one organism is nourishment for another.

Many plants rely on bees for pollination. The milkweed plant offers an exquisite example of mutuality. Its roots are anchored by soil, and it derives its food by photosynthesis. Butterflies and bees pollinate it. Milkweed responds by passing them nectar for energy and food. Caterpillars use the leaves for food, water, and shelter. The oxygen released by milkweed enables bees, butterflies, caterpillars, and many other creatures to convert their food into essential energy. More than 60% of the world's food is provided by crops pollinated by bees.

Photosynthesis is another example of how the rapidity and coordination of the Creation account make the start-up of nature's networks and complex cycles intelligible. Photosynthesis is essential for life on planet Earth and depends on sunlight.[3] It's a highly complex process involving approximately 100 ordered and organized proteins. Beginning in verse 3, Genesis chapter 1 rightly gives light a place of high priority. Plants, sunlight, and animals rapidly appear in succeeding days. Genesis gets the timing just right. It describes a harmonious plan in which photosynthesis was built into the fabric of plants and activated by sunlight just hours later for the benefit of animal life.

God's design is a harmonious brotherhood of living creatures where sharing, mutual support, and help give the advantage to all, and where altruism makes sense. This creation of grace stands in beneficent contrast to chance, the uncoordinated emergence of selfish genes from chemical space. The significance for us is to emulate God's purpose by caring for our environment and taking responsibility for the creatures with whom it is shared.

Though God is not part of the material universe, He is never represented as remote, unreachable, or uninterested. He appears as a Being vitally interested in His creation and desiring to interact with the first human pair. Adam and Eve were created "in the image of God" (Gen. 1:27), thereby promoting empathy with God so that not just a meaningful but an actually loving relationship could develop.

7

Intelligent Computational Agents Require a Designer

Germán H. Alférez

In *The Grand Design*, Hawking and Mlodinow state that "The example of Conway's *Game of Life* shows that even a very simple set of laws can produce complex features similar to those of intelligent life…. As in Conway's universe, the laws of our universe determine the evolution of the system, given the state at any one time."[1] According to Hawking and Mlodinow, preexisting physical laws are responsible for the complexity observed in intelligent beings. However, can even simple laws, just as the laws in Conway's *Game of Life*, be generated fortuitously? What do we learn about laws, design, and complexity from the world of computation?

The *Game of Life*

The *Game of Life*, also known simply as *Life*, is a cellular automaton devised by the mathematician John Horton Conway.[2] The universe of the *Game of Life* is an infinite, two-dimensional orthogonal grid of square cells, each of which is alive or dead. Every cell interacts with its eight neighbors according to Conway's simple genetic laws representing survivals, births, and deaths. The evolution of the game is defined by its initial configuration. The initial pattern of cells constitutes the seed of the system. The first generation is created by applying the genetic rules simultaneously to every cell in the seed. Births and deaths occur at the same time. The rules continue to be applied repeatedly to create further generations. Today, there are numerous computer programs to generate *Game of Life* configurations.

During the construction of the *Game of Life*, "Conway chose his rules carefully, after a long period of experimentation."[3] These rules were not the result of mere chance. In fact, in order to create intelligent computational agents able to produce complex features or behavior, it is necessary to establish rules that govern the game. No matter how simple they are, rules need to be established by someone.

The Complexity of Intelligent Computational Agents

In engineering, we are used to solving deterministic problems in which the solution solves the problem all the time (e.g., $1 + 1 = 2$). However, there are several problems in which the solution is not deterministic. For instance, the underlying software of an autonomous car needs to recognize whether an object is a stoplight. For humans, solving this kind of situation is easy. However, machines struggle in computer vision and other complex areas such as speech recognition.

Machine learning has emerged to solve these kinds of problems. Machine learning is a subfield of artificial intelligence that explores algorithms that can be said to "learn."[4] Someone could argue that machine learning has the potential to enable the auto-construction of software with programs that program themselves. As a result, programmers will become obsolete. However, even in that case, the algorithms that are used to create the predictive models of the "artificial programmer" need to be created by someone. The creation of such algorithms is not spontaneous, even in the case of the simplest classification algorithms that exhibit brilliance, such as the k-nearest neighbors algorithm. Neither is spontaneous self-creation the case with genetic algorithms and dynamic evolution of software.

In the case of genetic algorithms, which are inspired by Darwin's theory of evolution, it is necessary to clearly adjust the following rules to reach an optimal solution: (1) selection rules that select the parents who contribute to the population at the next generation; (2) crossover rules that combine two parents to form children for the next generation; and (3) mutation rules that apply random changes to particular parents to form children.[5]

Similarly, dynamic evolution of software is not accidental. Under the closed-world assumption, the possible events that an autonomous system has to face at runtime are fully known during construction. Nevertheless, it is difficult (or impossible) to foresee all the situations that could arise in the uncertain open world. In order to deal with unexpected events in the open world (e.g., surprise security threats), dynamic evolution of software supports the gradual or continuous growth of the software architecture. Dynamic evolution of software does not imply only punctual adaptations to punctual events, as dynamic adaptation in the closed world does, but a gradual structural or architectural growth into a better state. The construction of autonomous systems that support dynamic evolution requires the application of sophisticated methodologies and computational mechanisms.[6]

Conclusion

In any engineering project, design comes first and then construction follows. In the case of creating intelligent computational agents, engineers have to follow a strict methodology to collect the data that are going to be used to train them, prepare or clean the input data, create or reuse an artificial intelligence algorithm, develop predictive or descriptive models, test the model to measure its quality, and deploy the model. Every step involves extensive reasoning and complex construction.

No matter how much intelligence a computational agent displays, a designer is necessary to define the context of execution, the underlying laws or rules in this context, and the algorithm that indicates how the agent acts in the context. There is no such thing as chance in engineering. It can be said with confidence that rather than contradicting the need for a designer, intelligent computational agents are a great example of intelligent design.

PART II

Of Life and Molecules

8

The Matter of Life

Danilo Boskovic

Concepts regarding the origin of life from inanimate matter represent a profound philosophical problem that impacts our insight into ourselves and the world around us.[1] The problem, at least in part, may well be due to the general difficulty in defining what life is. While some thinkers view life as an elaborate, highly sophisticated machine,[2] others avoid such representations. Apparently, the rationale for this rejection is due to the fact that every machine has a maker and a purpose.[3] So, to compare life to a machine is to include both concepts implicitly. Therefore, various arguments are advanced with the specific objective of banishing all need for a purpose or a maker. As a result, one of two alternative approaches characterizes the majority of views about life's origins. On one hand, it is argued that Intellect + Matter → Life. On the other hand, supporters of the evolutionary perspective tend to favor the proposition that Matter → Life → Intellect.[4]

This latter view implies that information is the result of life rather than a requirement for it, and that, given enough time and favorable circumstances, matter itself—by chance—spontaneously gives rise to life, which can then be further molded by evolutionary processes. This is a faith position, because it is not clear what kind of evidence could either support or challenge it in the mind of the "faithful."

Intelligence is clearly the only well-demonstrated, known source of information. It is interesting that it never requires a great deal of effort to come to such a conclusion. No one reads a book without the implicit understanding that it had an author and probably an assortment of other ancillary participants such as secretaries, project managers, editors, publishers, promoters, and booksellers. Yet, we are expected to believe that the amount of genetic information present in a cell, from the most modest bacterium up to the level of human cells, somehow arose through processes no more involved than random chance and natural selection. This is asked of us, in spite of the presence of well-documented but underappreciated repair mechanisms, whose sole task is to maintain cellular genetic integrity in the face of physical, chemical, and biological hazards. Cells with flawed or weakened repair machinery are not observed somehow undergoing enhanced evolutionary progress. Instead, they are subject to faster senescence and death. Alternatively, if they cannot keep up with needed genetic repairs, cells may become cancerous, ultimately hastening death of the entire organism. Then, contrary to evolutionary thinking, this would suggest that integrity of genetic information is a requirement for life rather than merely a product of it.

Reports of spontaneous generation of some simple biomolecules more than 50 years ago are still used to bolster the arguments that life could arise under very primitive conditions, given availability of simple materials and adequate supply of energy[5] as well as some specialized environments and transport mechanisms.[6] However, even if this was somehow accomplished, it would still be a long way from an initiation of life. The reason is quite simple: it is easy for a living cell to die; it is not easy to bring a dead cell back to life. In fact, this has never been done, not even with a dead bacterium.

Consider an analogy with a symphony orchestra. Skilled artisans in specialized workshops or factories produce every musical instrument. But a pile of instruments does not an orchestra make. If we added a group of appropriately willing people, that would still be woefully insufficient. The people need to be skilled musicians for specific instruments. However, having access to highly skilled and motivated musicians, there is also a need for an appropriately orchestrated musical composition, hence the need for a composer. Specifically, each musician needs access to the musical partition suitable for his or her particular instrument. Then, there is the requirement for a maestro and a suitably comfortable and lit environment to serve as venue. Every one of these components requires a lot of deliberate, careful, dedicated effort. Nothing is left to happenstance. Yet, even the most beautifully played symphony pales in comparison to the level of functional complexity present even in a most modest bacterium.

To appreciate why it is hard to bring a dead bacterium back to life, consider what happens at its death. Perforating the cell membrane by some means, for example, results in the loss of a number of ion gradients across the membrane. Consequently, production of ATP, the energy currency for the cell, is stopped. All energy-requiring processes stop. All of the hundreds and thousands of internal reactions reach an equilibrium. At this stage, sealing of the membrane hole is a relatively simple task, and this may happen spontaneously. Yet the cell remains dead. To resurrect this cell, the various specific ion gradients need to be restored, and a critical number among the hundreds or thousands of reactions need to be reset so that they can productively function in a coordinated manner with each other. This is a technological nightmare.

Alternatively, resurrection could also be achieved by moving relative time backward. Resurrections simply cannot and do not occur spontaneously, even if most or all of the biomaterials are in place. From this perspective, the requirements for the origin of even the most primitive living cell are at least as daunting as the requirements for a resurrection. This is because prior to life's origin all the necessary biomaterials first need to come together. However, having biomaterials and all the genetic information, though necessary, is not sufficient. All constituents need to be in just the right concentrations so that numerous key reactions, among thousands, are reset to their respective dynamic steady states.

The various models for the origin of life will likely continue to be promoted until a deeper appreciation takes hold about what life actually is. Is it something akin to musical instruments, the musicians, or the orchestration? Or, is it like the music of a well-played symphony?

9

Origin of Life:
By Design or Chemical Evolution?

Elena Titova

The defenders of the hypothesis of chemical evolution (abiogenesis) believe that about four billion years ago, biological molecules, first simple ones, then more complex, began to naturally assemble on the earth. They spontaneously combined to form cellular organelles and primitive protocells in the primary ocean ("broth").

The defenders of the abiogenesis hypothesis believe that organic substances formed from inorganic components in the atmosphere under the action of radiation or electrical discharges.[1] They consider that the early atmosphere was generally reducing. In this case, biologically significant organic matter, as it is known, would be destroyed by ultraviolet radiation in an atmosphere devoid of oxygen and the shielding protection of an ozone layer. Other scenarios suggest the first organic matter could have come from space or been synthesized near submerged volcanoes and deep-sea vents.[2]

If amino acids (protein monomers) could move to the broth through highly hypothetical processes, as substances with high reactivity, they would actively interact with aldehydes, acids, bases, and other compounds that are expected to be present in the broth. There would be an unimaginable mixture of all sorts of organic compounds, in which substances necessary for biological components would be a negligible fraction. These compounds would spontaneously react with each other in different ways in the presence of activators and inhibitors, resulting in the formation of tar-like mixtures not capable of further reactions relevant to the origin of life.

In order for amino acids to form peptides (several monomers) or proteins (polymers with specific properties) suitable for living systems, the reactions between initial substances must be strictly selective on a number of points:

- Monomers must be only α-amino acids (i.e., the H_2N- amino group and COOH- carboxyl group are connected only to the first α-carbon atom).

- Monomers must be only L-spatial (levorotatory, or "left-handed") forms of amino acids. D-spatial (dextrorotatory, or "right-handed") forms are not included in cell proteins because they inhibit the formation of their tertiary structure, which is necessary for functional activity. In laboratory syntheses, D- and L-forms of a specific amino acid are formed in equal amounts.[3] Both forms are chemically equivalent. Therefore, L-amino acids could not selectively be included in the protein structure.

- Only 20 types of amino acids are involved in protein synthesis, out of more than 300 that could be formed in undirected chemical reactions.

- To obtain peptides (proteins), only peptide bonds must occur between amino acids. The laboratory synthesis of even one dipeptide is complex and must be strictly controlled by blocking amino and carboxyl groups with protective groups, which are not involved in the formation of a peptide bond, and activating carboxyl groups, which are involved in the reaction.[4] In addition, the spontaneous formation of peptide bonds in the broth is impossible because one of the reaction products is water.

- Amino acids must be arranged in strict linear sequence; an amino acid chain must not have branches and cycles.

Notice that these peptide-forming reactions do not flow spontaneously but require a continuous supply of energy in a useful form.

The probability of the random formation of a sequence of several hundred amino acids for a functional protein is so low as to be mathematically incredible.[5] All this indisputably points to the necessity of intelligent design in the origins of enzymatic synthesis of proteins using information recorded in the DNA. Spontaneous processes and chance do not have the selectivity required for a purposeful arrangement of reaction products.

What about nucleotides (monomers of nucleic acids)? Nucleotides include a nitrogenous base, sugar (monosaccharides ribose for RNA and deoxyribose for DNA in only D-spatial forms) and phosphate. In the simulated primordial atmosphere, some nitrogenous bases (but not ribose and deoxyribose), very unstable and with a low yield of reaction products, can be "spontaneously" obtained from pure initial substances. However, organic syntheses of biomolecules under strict laboratory conditions are not spontaneous processes. They demonstrate the input of a scientist's intelligent intervention in the experimental setup and involve the use of chemically pure initial compounds, as well as purification and extraction of intermediate products, which are unwarranted processes to assume for the so-called primitive Earth. In addition, all abiogenic syntheses lead to a mixture of spatial D- and L-monosaccharides. Nitrogenous bases, sugars, and phosphates do not spontaneously assemble into nucleotides. Besides, different nucleotide components require completely different conditions for their formation. This represents a major roadblock for the spontaneous assembly of polymers in the broth (or anywhere else).

What about the formation of nucleic acids? In model experiments, DNA and RNA have not been produced. In living systems, replication (doubling) of both DNA and RNA occurs only through a precisely arranged enzymatic matrix, so that adjacent nucleotides are linked only in a specific way. This is, to me, evidence of the Creator's design for life.

In living organisms, the systems of syntheses of nucleic acids and proteins, as well as storage of energy in the form of adenosine triphosphate (ATP) via an intricate biochemical mechanism, are interconnected and interdependent. DNA and RNA syntheses require enzyme and energy provision, while the enzymes of ATP and nucleic acid syntheses are encoded in DNA. There is no reasonable explanation other than their simultaneous appearance is the outcome of the Creator's majestic design.

There is no reason to consider chemical evolution as an established fact. The evolutionary chain from randomly generated biological molecules to cells is not supported by scientific data and appears speculative at best. This hypothesis is filled with impossible events, for which the probability is essentially zero. The most rational explanation for the origin of life that is consistent with scientific facts is the recognition of the work of an Almighty and Intelligent Creator.

10 ●

DNA's Designer Alphabet

During the winter months of 1869, the Swiss doctor Friedrich Miescher was hard at work in his laboratory at the University of Tübingen. He was studying the chemical composition of cells in pus-soaked surgical bandages that he had retrieved from the hospital garbage. There, he discovered a new microscopic substance that was not a protein or a lipid. Since the substance originated in the nucleus of the cells, he called it "nuclein." Dr. Miescher even wondered whether this substance might be responsible for the traits that organisms inherit from their parents, but later dismissed this idea.[1]

It would take another 75 years before Francis Crick and James Watson would shine their X-ray spotlights along the coiled strands of nuclein and claim a Nobel Prize for figuring out the double helix structure of one of the world's most iconic molecules: deoxyribonucleic acid (DNA).

While the discovery of DNA and its structure is scientifically exhilarating, what it encodes is even more stunning. DNA literally contains the code for all of life on Earth. It reveals that life is not just physics and chemistry, but also includes information at its most basic level. As Richard Dawkins has observed,

> After Watson and Crick, we know that genes themselves, within their minute internal structure, are long strings of pure digital information. What is more, they are truly digital, in the full and strong sense of computers and compact disks, not in the weak sense of the nervous system. The genetic code is not a binary code as in computers, nor an eight-level code as in some telephone systems, but a

quaternary code, with four symbols. The machine code of the genes is uncannily computerlike.[2]

In short, DNA functions as an information system that encodes, stores, and retrieves the information needed for life itself.

One of the most fundamental features of an information system is that it uses an alphabet to encode information. DNA is no exception. In particular, it uses four nucleotides called adenine, cytosine, thymine, and guanine, which are represented by the letters A, C, T, and G. This alphabet is so fundamental and firmly established in our genetic thinking that we hardly give it a second thought.

However, I would like to invite you to stop and reflect on this alphabet for a while. We all know of other alphabets, such as the binary alphabet used in computer systems, which uses 0's and 1's, and the English alphabet which has twenty-six letters. The question that immediately springs to mind is this: why does the genetic alphabet have four nucleotide letters?

The Hungarian theoretical evolutionary biologist Eörs Szathmáry asked that very question.[3] By undertaking an information-theoretic study of the genetic information system, he was able to show that a four-letter genetic alphabet is optimal with respect to a compromise between two factors: copying fidelity and catalytic efficiency. As the size of the genetic alphabet increases, the catalytic efficiency increases. However, as the alphabet size increases, the copying fidelity decreases. Thus, Szathmáry proposed that the genetic alphabet is a frozen evolutionary optimum from the hypothesized RNA world in which life was supposed to have originated.[4] One is tempted to observe that the term "frozen evolutionary" is an oxymoron. It is reassuring to know, though, that the alphabet that encodes everything about us, together with **A**ardvarks, **B**obcats, **C**oyotes, and so on, all the way down to **Z**ebras, really is optimal.

Even though our genetic alphabet does seem rather frozen in our biosphere, it raises the question whether it could have been otherwise. Indeed, biochemists have been actively pursuing the possibility of expanding the genetic alphabet, and in February 2019, Steven

Benner and a broad team of researchers achieved just that. They expanded the genetic alphabet from four to eight. By making small adjustments to the molecular structure of the standard nucleotides, they were able to create four new nucleotides, which they represented by the letters S, B, P, and Z.[5]

Benner's expanded genetic alphabet shows that the standard genetic alphabet is not the only one physically possible. So where did it come from originally?

There are four explanations for the origin of the genetic alphabet:

1. It is physically necessary for the genetic alphabet to have four nucleotide letters. The research work of Benner and his team in expanding the genetic alphabet has demonstrated that this explanation is not true.[6]

2. The genetic alphabet contains four nucleotide letters by chance. The information-theoretic research work of Szathmáry has demonstrated that the size of the genetic alphabet is optimal and the probability that the optimal four-letter alphabet would be landed on simply by chance is vanishingly small. Other explanations are therefore more likely to be true.

3. The four-letter genetic alphabet evolved. The difficulty with this explanation is that there is no empirical evidence that the genetic alphabet evolved. Evolution requires a self-replicating mechanism, but this requires an information system that is based on an alphabet. There is no evidence that any proto-genetic alphabet existed. Therefore, for the genetic alphabet to evolve, it would have required some form of chemical evolution process. It must be emphasized, though, that we have no empirical evidence of this chemical evolution process. It is fair to say that all chemical evolutionary explanations for the origins of life have reached an impasse.

4. The genetic alphabet was intelligently designed. Like every other alphabet that we know of, including the expansion of the genetic alphabet that Benner and colleagues have achieved, this is the most satisfactory explanation for the genetic alphabet.

As he went about his experiments in Tübingen in 1869, Miescher stumbled upon the molecule that stores the information of life. At the very foundation of this information is an alphabet that points beyond its empirical letters to the Designer of life itself.

11

DNA: A Magnificent Nanomolecule

Orlex B. Yllano

When I was a kid, my interest in natural sciences was stirred to life when my science teacher said that "molecules are moving." From then on, my motivation was to understand how God's intelligent designs work in nature. I ended up pursuing science and working on DNA.

Deoxyribonucleic acid, commonly known as DNA, is a tiny molecule with a diameter of 1.8 to 2.3 nm and a pitch of 3.4 nm. To have an idea of how small DNA is, consider that one nanometer is one-billionth of a meter. More than 10,000 DNA strands could fit in the width of a human hair. DNA is located inside the nucleus of the cell and consists of two chains that twist around each other like a winding ladder, stabilized by the highly specific pairing of molecules called "base pairs." There are 10–12 base pairs per helical turn.[1]

The DNA structure is kept together by two hydrogen bonds between adenine (A) and thymine (T) and three hydrogen bonds between cytosine (C) and guanine (G). It has pentose deoxyribose sugar and a phosphate backbone joined by covalent bonds, which make the molecule stable.

The DNA inside each of our cells is too small to be seen with the naked eye. However, if straightened out, the total DNA in a human cell would stretch to about 1.5–3.0 m.[2] Since the human genome (the totality of an organism's hereditary information) contains around three billion base pairs of DNA in 46 chromosomes in about 10^{13} cells of the body, the total length of DNA present in an adult human being is about $2×10^{13}$ m,[3] long enough to wrap around the earth 500,000 times. Thus, DNA is considered one of the most extended molecules on Earth. In spite of this very long configuration, it is well designed to fit inside the nucleus of a cell without distorting the encoded information. It has a stunning coiling ability too. The folded and packed DNA molecule is approximately 10,000 times shorter than its linear form.[4] Even though this nanomolecule is tightly packed, it can quickly unpack when the right signal is recognized by the cell. Remarkably, the uncoiling of DNA requires accurate sequential actions of topoisomerases to unpack the DNA supercoils.

Approximately 99.5% of DNA is similar in all humans, but the way it functions can vary greatly.[5] In other words, although we all have almost similar DNA make-up, if these DNA sequences are differentially processed from each other, we end up having different faces, complexions, hair patterns, and eye colors. This makes each person phenotypically and genotypically unique. The uniqueness of the DNA sequence between and among species is utilized in fingerprinting individuals with a high degree of accuracy.

The processing of DNA occurs in an intricate step-by-step fashion. The parent DNA is replicated, and the information is copied to a molecule known as messenger RNA (mRNA) inside the nucleus of the cell. When the RNA is mature (after the addition of 5' methylated guanine cap and adenosine residues at the 3' end), mRNA leaves the nucleus and goes out into the cytoplasm of the cell, and here mRNA is translated to protein by the aid of the ribosomes and several enzymes. The generated protein is then further modified to perform specific tasks inside the cell, following a very orderly and precise method. A system has been provided to correct replication errors along the way. In some instances where an incorrect base is added, an enzyme, DNA polymerase, proofreads the base that has just been added and correspondingly corrects and replaces it with the correct nucleotide base. Where some errors are not corrected during replication, mismatch repair enzymes recognize the incorrectly added nucleotide, excise it, and then replace it with the correct one. These intricate delivery systems and the extraordinary degree of timing and accuracy of these processes are hallmarks of intelligent design.

The astounding properties of this biopolymer captivated the minds of scientists and bioengineers. Using the DNA origami approach, one can envision and create any design in the laboratory.[6] DNA could be used to construct and organize nanoscale gold rods into larger structures.[7] It can also be used to fuel molecular machines.[8] When two complementary strands of DNA combine, about 70 MeV of free energy is released as each base pair is formed.[9] This energy is enough to power a nanoscale device. The above nanotechnological advancements along with DNA 3D structure, DNA tweezer, supramolecular DNA assembly, and creation of new DNA motifs are anchored on DNA's complexity, aperiodicity, and ease of self-assembly, which could revolutionize molecular-scale electronics and nanomedicine.[10]

Interestingly, DNA is also a superior storage material of information. It stores specific instructions on the myriad processes of life. DNA can hold an enormous amount of information compared to the current data storage capacity of computer hard drives. Because of the immense capacity of DNA to store information, it is now recognized as the storage medium with the highest known information density.[11] The sophisticated design of this nanomolecule makes it suitable to store the instructions for all life.

This magnificent nanomolecule inside a tiny cell is a natural wonder in which God's instruction manual and the blueprint of life of all living creatures reside. In particular, the synchronous processes during DNA replication, transcription, and translation orchestrated by myriad biomolecules in a fraction of a second with unprecedented timing and accuracy testify to intelligent design. The intricate design of DNA, its stability, flexibility, ability to store information, and associated orderly processes point to the great and intelligent Designer who created all things in the vast universe.

12

A Look at the Mirror: Chirality in Organic Molecules

Nelson C. Martins

You have certainly looked at the mirror countless times, yet have you ever noticed that the image you see is not exactly like you? If you are wearing a shirt with lettering, words will be written backward in the mirror. So, the image you see is not really you, but your *mirror* image. Although this doesn't seem like much of a difference, it has major implications in chemistry, especially in biological systems.

When a molecule and its mirror image are not superimposable, due to a somewhat different three-dimensional arrangement, the molecule is said to be chiral—based on the ancient Greek word for hand. Indeed, this reminds us of our hands, one being like the mirror image of the other, yet non-superimposable. The two antipodes—the molecule and its mirror image—are said to be enantiomers and may have their respective chiral configuration indicated with the prefixes D- and L-, which stand for *dexter* and *laevo*, respectively, right and left in Latin.

The property of chirality, or handedness, is displayed by a great number of organic molecules presenting at least a chiral center, a chiral axis, or a chiral plane.[1] In fact, chirality is a pervading feature, with nearly 50% of molecules in living organisms being chiral. Moreover, biological systems are homochiral, appearing just in the L or D form through all the biosphere.[2] In other words, in living organisms, only L-amino acids and D-carbohydrates are present, not the corresponding mirror image, D-amino acids and L-carbohydrates.

Owing to homochirality, biological systems are able to discriminate enantiomeric compounds; thus a living organism may have a specific response toward one enantiomer and a dissimilar one toward the other optical isomer.[3] Insect pheromones, plant growth regulators, pesticides, and drugs are among some of these natural or human-made compounds.[4] For example, L,L-aspartame (see Figure 12-1), is perceived by us as having a very sweet taste, whereas the

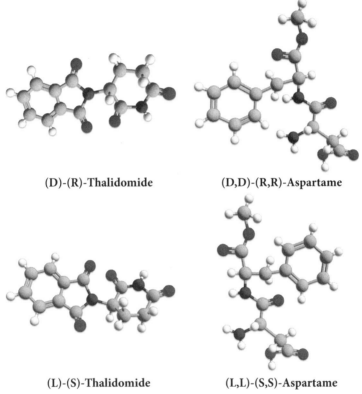

(D)-(R)-Thalidomide   **(D,D)-(R,R)-Aspartame**

(L)-(S)-Thalidomide   **(L,L)-(S,S)-Aspartame**

FIGURE 12-1. Enantiomers of thalidomide and aspartame (hydrogen in white, c1arbon in light gray, oxygen in gray, and nitrogen in dark gray). The thalidomide molecule has only one chiral center, namely, the carbon that connects the two heteroatom rings via a C-N bond. The two enantiomers differ only in the configuration of that carbon. Instead, aspartame has two chiral centers and thus four possible chiral configurations, yet only one binds with the right tongue receptors to be perceived as sweet.

D,D-isomer tastes bitter. In pharmaceutical drugs, an enantiomeric substance may exhibit highly beneficial therapeutic effects while its mirror image compound can be toxic or even mutagenic. This is due to the precise molecular recognition characteristics of natural binding sites in protein enzymes, receptors, and transport systems.[5] Widely known is the case of thalidomide, where the D form of the drug is a mild analgesic, and the L form is a powerful teratogen.[6]

While it is clear that chirality plays an important role in life, the major question to be answered is about the origin of homochirality in biological systems. As a matter of fact, to have a substance that is enantiopure, that is, that presents only one of the possible optical isomers for a specific compound, either that isomer was selectively formed or the racemate, the 1:1 mixture of optical isomers, needs to be separated through a process called chiral resolution. Interestingly, both situations normally rely on the use of other enantiopure chiral auxiliaries.[7]

I have worked for a number of years with asymmetric catalysis, preparing chiral ligands and catalysts and performing catalytic reactions in order to synthesize enantioenriched and enantiopure compounds. This experience has impressed me with how much thought and research is needed to design and develop efficient asymmetric catalytic systems, even when using chiral enantiopure auxiliaries.

Producing pure optically active substances already presents its challenges to chemists, but what we see in living organisms goes much beyond in terms of complexity. Macromolecules and polymers made up of homochiral units form complex structures, such as the DNA helix—homochiral itself—which in turn interact in multipart and intricate systems necessary for life.

The naturalistic scenario, in which life is not created by a Designer but emerges by chance, is then faced with a question that still lacks a definite answer: If living matter evolved in prebiotic times from chiral molecules formed out of simple achiral precursors, how did this [chiral] resolution appear?[8]

Questions may arise regarding why do we not find homochiral biological systems with D-amino acids and L-carbohydrates, or even with other combinations such as DD or LL. After all, in a blind chiral resolution scenario, would it not be expected that different combinations of homochiral compounds would be formed?

When considering the chemistry of life, we can clearly see the uniqueness of each compound that makes us alive. Homochirality in biological systems further reflects the fine-tuning of the conditions needed for living organisms to exist on Earth, adding to the array of factors that make the probability for life originating without design infinitesimal. To me, looking at the mirror from the perspective of chemistry and biochemistry clearly reveals that there is a Designer behind our existence.

13

Membrane Asymmetry Points to the Creator

Carrie A. C. Wolfe

As a chemistry professor, when I study nature I see evidence of God as Creator. I have been teaching biochemistry for many years and often teach about the structure and function of cellular membranes. The cellular membrane in living cells is composed of lipids and proteins as well as some carbohydrates. The plasma membrane of animals and bacteria is a lipid bilayer that serves as a barrier between the inside of each living cell and its environment. One of the leaflets of the lipid bilayer is exposed to the outside of the cell, and the other leaflet is exposed to the inside of the cell, or the cytoplasmic side. The two leaflets are very different in composition—they are asymmetrical.

Typical lipids in the cell membrane are phospholipids such as glycolipids, sphingomyelin, phosphatidylserine, phosphatidylcholine, and phosphatidylinositol. In living cells, these types of lipids are not randomly distributed between the two bilayers. Glycolipids contain carbohydrates and are always found on the outer leaflet of the plasma membrane. They are never found on the layer that faces the cytoplasm. Sphingomyelin is also almost always found in this outer leaflet. Phosphatidylserine, however, is found primarily in the opposite side of the bilayer—the inner leaflet. How does this asymmetry arise? In the lab, when researchers work to assemble a lipid bilayer, the phospholipids and glycolipids self-assemble in a random symmetrical manner, producing a bilayer membrane with no asymmetry.[1]

Many proteins are found in biological membranes. Some are positioned across the membrane and are exposed on both sides (both the cytoplasmic side and the exterior of the cell). These are called transmembrane proteins. Some are pumps and channels, and others are receptor proteins. These proteins need to be oriented in the membrane the correct way. For example, if the ligand-binding site of the receptor protein is facing the extracellular environment and is able to bind to a hormone molecule, it will change the 3D structure of the transmembrane protein, allowing the signal to be noticed and transmitted to the inside of the living cell.

Pumps and channels must be correctly oriented in the bilayer so the ions, or molecules, being moved across the cell membrane are transported the correct way. For example, the sodium-potassium ATPase is an important pump in many cells. It always pumps sodium ions out of the cell while it pumps potassium ions into the cell. This pump requires the use of ATP (cellular energy) to pump these ions across the membrane, setting up an ion gradient. The ion gradient can then be used by other transmembrane proteins called secondary transporters to pump other important molecules or ions across the membrane. One example is the sodium-glucose linked transporter, which uses the sodium gradient to pump glucose into the cell; sodium is allowed into the cell through this transporter as glucose is pumped in. These protein pumps and transporters never "flip" in orientation— that is, protein channels and pumps do not experience "transverse diffusion." Scientists have never found these proteins inserted into the membrane the wrong way. These specifically oriented proteins are another example of the asymmetry of cellular membranes.

However, phospholipids are able to occasionally flip from one leaflet of the bilayer to the other, undergoing spontaneous transverse diffusion. This flipping diminishes the asymmetry; after a phospholipid flips into the wrong leaflet, it is usually placed back into its original leaflet by special proteins in the cell membrane called flippases. For example, phosphatidylserine is found mostly on the inner leaflet of the plasma membrane. When it flips to the leaflet facing the exterior of the cell, the flippase notices the phosphatidylserine molecule in the wrong place and flips it back to the inner leaflet. This is important for the cell because when phagocytes (macrophages) notice phosphatidylserine molecules exposed to the outside of a cell, they recognize this and assume the cell has experienced apoptosis (cell death). Phagocytes are signaled to destroy and remove a cell that has phosphatidylserine in the outer bilayer.[2] In this case, the asymmetry of the phosphatidylserine excluded from the outer leaflet saves the cell from being destroyed by other cells.

Another attribute of the asymmetrical distribution of the phospholipids in a cellular membrane is the intrinsic membrane potential, or non-zero transmembrane potential, of the plasma membrane in living cells. This membrane potential is caused by the positively charged "head groups" of phosphatidylcholine and sphingomyelin on the extracellular side of the plasma membrane and the net negatively charged head group of phosphatidylserine that is almost entirely on the inner leaflet. This transmembrane potential is linked to varied physiological phenomena.[3]

I have wondered how this asymmetry was originally set up in a cell. A cell would not be able to function for long if the phospholipids (such as phosphatidylserine) and protein channels or pumps were inserted randomly into the cell membrane. If the asymmetry wasn't initially present in a living cell membrane, the ion gradients needed for other cellular processes would never be established, and the cell would quickly die. While thinking about this problem, I was stopped in my tracks when I read this line in my biochemistry textbook: "This absolute asymmetry is preserved because membrane proteins do not rotate from one side of the membrane to the other and because membranes are always synthesized by the growth of preexisting membranes."[4]

This implies that there must always be a preexisting membrane from which further cellular membranes may grow. This information fits a model in which a Creator could design and create the original cell membranes with absolute asymmetry of the lipids and proteins in them.

14

Conserved throughout Creation

José A. Cardé-Serrano

Evolution means change. Textbooks in all biological disciplines state that organisms change throughout time, acquiring new characteristics that fit them best to adapt to the environment. However, if the basic engine of evolution is change, why are so many important molecular features so similar in different species that have supposedly been subjected to hundreds of millions of years of evolution? Ever since I started graduate school, I have been amazed by numerous instances where the phrase "highly conserved throughout evolution" is used to "explain" the striking similarities that distinctly different types of organism share at the molecular level. This essay presents a few examples of systems described as "conserved throughout evolution," arguing that they rather illustrate the wisdom and greatness of an Intelligent Designer.

Histones

The histones are a group of four (H2A, H2B, H3, and H4) basic, positively charged proteins. Two units of each one of them form the nucleosome, a very important structure that plays a key role in chromatin condensation and regulation of genetic expression. To have an idea of what condensation means, think about storing a 2-m-long DNA string inside a 6-μm capsule (nucleus) that has to be enclosed in a 25-μm diameter cell.[1] At this condensation level, a soccer ball would contain enough DNA to cover the distance between the earth and the sun more than 650 times. The interaction between the histone tails and the DNA is important also for the efficient utilization of genetic information by means of replication and transcription present in all eukaryotic cells.

When the amino acid sequences of histones of different organisms were analyzed, scientists concluded that they had been "highly conserved throughout evolution," because of their high level of similarity in a whole range of organisms from plants to mammals.[2] This conservation includes both the part of the sequence that participates in the DNA folding as well as the part that participates in the regulation of gene expression. These similarities can be explained as the result of Creation by the same Designer. When God designed the nucleus of the eukaryotic cell, He addressed the issue of how to pack its DNA and created the histones. He fine-tuned (2%–20% change) the sequences for the same purpose in different organisms.

Nonsense-Mediated Decay (NMD)

Nonsense-Mediated Decay (NMD) is one of several quality control surveillance systems in cells guaranteeing that the mRNAs translated into proteins are of the appropriate length and that their translation product will be fully functional. The NMD system was first discovered in yeast and nematodes, but has since been documented in all eukaryotes. Several diseases have been associated with aberrant mRNAs that escape this surveillance system.[3] NMD also serves as a fundamental post-transcriptional regulatory mechanism for eukaryotic gene expression. NMD depends on three proteins known as UPF1, UPF2, and UPF3 in yeast. UPF1 participates in the surveillance of the defective mRNA as part of the SURF complex. UPF2 and UPF3 participate more specifically along with UPF1 as part of a complex known as DECID in the degradation of aberrant mRNAs. In organisms as different as yeast, nematodes, fruit flies, and humans, the same mechanism is performed by a set of three similar proteins with the same specific function: surveillance and degradation of aberrant mRNAs. The amino acid sequences and domains of the proteins, as expected, are highly conserved. Again, these similarities can be interpreted as evidence of common design.

Homeobox Genes (Hox)

The Hox genes are so named because mutations in them cause homeotic transformations.[4] In fruit flies these genes determine the identity of insect body segments following the anterior/posterior axis. Researchers have shown that mutations of these Hox genes can put a leg where the antenna should be and make eyes appears on flies' legs. Experiments comparing Hox genes in chickens and mice showed that the genes controlling where thoracic vertebrae are converted to lumbar vertebrae (not articulating with ribs) are the same.

Even more interesting is that both insects and humans, organisms that are anatomically very different, have several genes in common. In humans, as in fruit flies, these genes control the development of our head to tail anatomy in embryos. Similar genes controlling the development of eyes of insects and humans have been discovered. Development of the eye in mammalian embryos is regulated by the *Pax 6* Hox gene. In *Drosophila* (fruit flies) the *Pax 6*-like gene is *eyeless*. Loss-of-function mutations of *Pax 6* result in syndromes affecting eye development, and in *eyeless*, result in loss of eyes in adult flies. *Pax*-like proteins are found in all higher metazoans and are transcriptional regulators involved in eye formation in all bilaterian animals.[5]

The evolutionary scenario requires that after supposedly 600 million years of evolution of the eye, the genes regulating eye development did not change much, yet produced eyes with radically different structures.

Conclusion

The three examples discussed here are just a few of the hundreds that are routinely presented as "conserved throughout evolution," and the list continues to grow. Every time I run into a scientific article or textbook addressing an important mechanism as "conserved throughout evolution," I see it as evidence of an Intelligent Designer who creates what is appropriate for life and uses that basic model for different types of creatures. It can be concluded that all these processes, genes, and proteins are rather "conserved throughout creation," because they are intelligently designed to be applicable in a variety of living organisms.

15

Cholesterol:
The Wonder of Biosynthesis

Glenn Phillips

Since its discovery from gallstones in 1769 by Francois Poulletier de la Salle, cholesterol (see Figure 15-1) has attracted the attention of scientists. As early as 1932, the first total synthesis was attempted, and by 1949 two very famous groups were competing to be the first to synthesize cholesterol. In 1951, the first synthetic route was published by Robinson and Cornforth.[1] The following year, another synthesis was published by Woodward and Sondheimer.[2] Since then, at least three other synthetic routes have been reported with the final product either being a racemic (50:50) mixture of the natural product and its enantiomer (non-superimposable mirror image) or just pure enantiomer, *ent*-cholesterol.

Each of the chemical routes to synthesis started with a naturally occurring compound that could either be extracted from natural sources or bought from a chemical company that synthesized the starting material from an even simpler natural product. Numerous intermediates, including various catalysts, reagents, and other substrates, also had to be purchased or prepared. The shortest reported route to *ent*-cholesterol (not the naturally occurring compound) consists of 16 linear steps with a 2% overall yield from the starting compound (S)-citronellol.[3] The work by Rychnovsky and Belani introduces the AB rings of cholesterol using annulation (ring forming reaction) that closely resembles Sir Robert Robinson's annulation reaction. The synthesis of pure, naturally occurring cholesterol took many more steps, and the yield was also minuscule compared to the volume of starting material used.[4] In mammals, cholesterol is synthesized mainly in the liver, adrenal glands, intestines, and gonads.[5] Its entire carbon backbone is made from one molecule, an acetyl group (CH_3CO). The first stage of biological synthesis utilizes three acetyl groups and the enzyme coenzyme A to produce mevalonate, a six-carbon intermediate. The next step involves adding three phosphates (PO_4^{3-}) to the two hydroxyl (OH) groups using a kinase (the enzyme) and three adenosine triphosphates (ATPs). Initially, kinase just phosphorylates (adds a phosphate group) and later performs phosphorylation and decarboxylation (removal of carbon dioxide).

The product isopentyl pyrophosphate (IPP) is the result of this decarboxylation. Some of the IPP is stored in that form, while a larger portion is converted to dimethylallyl pyrophosphate (DMAPP) by a process called isomerization. In this isomerization, an external double bond is moved internally. With both isoprene units (a five-carbon unit with four carbons in a straight line and a CH_3 group on carbon number 2) at hand, the isomers are combined to produce geranyl pyrophosphate. One more DMAPP is added to make the

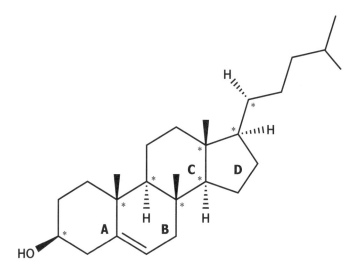

FIGURE 15-1. Structure of cholesterol. Asterisks denote chiral centers.

15-carbon farnesyl pyrophosphate. Another farnesyl pyrophosphate produced in an identical fashion is added to the first to make squalene, with 30 carbons.

Squalene has all the carbons needed to make cholesterol, but the famous ABCD four-ringed structure has not been formed. To achieve this, one of the two double bonds at the end of the squalene chain out of a possible six choices is oxidized with O_2 and nicotinamide adenine dinucleotide phosphate (NADPH) to make squalene oxide. Cleavage of the oxide activates a beautiful cascade reaction in which all the internal double bounds of squalene react in sequence to form the ABCD steroid ring system.

Lanosterol is the next major intermediate. It is formed via a number of hydride and methyl group shifts and an elimination of hydrogen to produce the double bond. It takes another 19 steps to form cholesterol. These steps include the removal of three of the eight methyl groups present in lanosterol (demethylation), plus addition and removal of double bonds. Although this may seem like a lot of steps, the effort is worthwhile because many of these intermediates are used to make other useful molecules such as vitamin D, fatty acids, and other steroids.

Cholesterol has eight chiral centers, which means that based on chirality alone, a possible 256 (2^n; n = number of chiral centers) compounds could be synthesized in the body. However, only one isomer is produced. The body metabolism is designed to determine how each isoprene unit should be stored and assembled, as well as how to differentiate between the six double bonds in squalene and the eight methyl groups in lanosterol. The enzyme's selectivity and specificity is astounding from the perspective of a synthetic organic chemist.

Many of the scientific queries regarding the biosynthetic pathway of cholesterol can be specifically answered. Where is cholesterol made? In the liver, adrenal glands, intestines, and gonads. What is cholesterol made from? From manipulation of one molecule, an acetyl group. How is it made? Through a complex sequence of steps, detailed above.

Two questions remain unanswered at this point: When was cholesterol first made, and by whom? If the scientific community considered it appropriate to honor with Nobel Prizes the synthetic feats of Sir Robert Robinson, John Cornforth, and Robert B. Woodward, a truly scientific mind must ask the same question about nature. Who created these synthetic pathways? Considering this is just one of an uncounted number of compounds necessary for life, I propose that the real prize belongs to the Author of life and nature.

PART III

A Green World

16

All Natural Chemistry: Not What You Think!

Ryan T. Hayes

What is a natural chemical reaction? Are all the chemical reactions found on planet Earth considered to be natural? If not, how does one decide what is naturally occurring or not? The way we speak about "nature" and "natural" leads scientists and non-scientists to a confusing and inconsistent way of applying these words. Understanding the limits of spontaneous chemical reactions informs on what can happen naturally, or without additional energy or engineered contrivances. I would like to propose that cyanobacteria, plants, and any other photosynthetic organisms can be considered unnatural chemical factories since they combine a series of unfavorable reactions to make unnatural end products.

There are many important chemical reactions happening around us all the time, some of which are spontaneous. How does one discover whether a reaction is spontaneous or not? Chemists define spontaneous reactions as those whose Gibbs free energy is favorable based on the combination of enthalpy (emitting or absorbing heat) and entropy (spreading out or coming together of atoms), along with the temperature. All chemical reactions fall into four categories that are combinations of the two enthalpy options and the two entropy options. Three types are spontaneous. The fourth non-spontaneous category describes much of the reactions found in living systems, and no amount of time, temperature, and energy can make these happen. Only a coordinated effort involving the proper ingredients, concentrations, viscosity, mixing, temperature, type of energy, pH, purity, and proper molecular geometry will make these non-spontaneous reactions happen. Intelligence is able to devise a way to make these reactions happen. Photosynthesis falls under this non-spontaneous category along with a number of critical life-supporting reactions such as the formation of DNA, RNA, and proteins.

In order for photosynthesis to work, at least eight subsystems need to be in place at the right time and place. This is another example of molecular irreducible complexity as defined by Behe and others.[1] The ingredients, carbon dioxide and water, need to be placed in the correct chemical location and amounts along with the proper temperature in order to manufacture glucose and oxygen.

Photosystem I subsystem needs 417 chemical components that are specifically arranged and aligned to capture light and begin the process of creating chemical energy. These 417 molecules consist of beta-carotenes and porphyrin molecules that have to be precisely positioned in order to collect sunlight of the proper energy and funnel it to the correct location. If the molecular spacing and relative orientations are off by the distance of a few atoms, the process will not work. Porphyrins (chlorophyll) are some of the best molecules known to humans at absorbing light, and these just so happen to be what are found inside of Photosystem I.

Photosystem II is not much simpler.[2] Photosystem II (of cyanobacteria and green plants) is composed of around 20 subunits as well as other accessory, light-harvesting proteins. Each Photosystem II contains at least 99 cofactors comprised of 35 chlorophyll a, 12 beta-carotenes, two pheophytins, two plastoquinones, two hemes, one bicarbonate, 20 lipid molecules, the Mn_4CaO_5 cluster, one non-heme Fe^{2+}, and two putative Ca^{2+} ions per monomer. Most of these molecules need to be created and precisely positioned by the organism.

ATP synthase, cytochrome B6F, plastaquinone, plastocyanon, ferredoxin, and ferredoxin NADP+ reductase are all needed, finely tuned, and full of specialized chemicals as with Photosystems I and II. All of these systems need to be embedded in a membrane in the correct orientation and spacing to work together. The glycolic cycle is populated during this process to continually produce various chemicals such as glucose, which the photosynthetic organism uses as a structural chemical and energy storage.

According to the Darwinian narrative, bacteria figured out how to get energy from sulfur, methane, or some other chemicals next to thermal vents in the ocean, and then through natural selection and adaptation, they discovered how to manufacture glucose and dioxygen from carbon dioxide and water using photosynthesis. This process seems so naturally straightforward, how could it be wrong? Unfortunately, the actual chemistry of photosynthesis within living systems does not occur spontaneously. A brief but careful look at photosynthesis quickly shows that it is not possible to design and successfully implement this irreducibly complex set of chemical parts and chemical reactions without the involvement of intelligence.

Most of the chemical parts to the photosynthetic reaction center require intelligent design to make. These chemicals need to be manufactured within the plant by proteins and enzymes and then taken to the exact location where they will be used, properly positioned, and correctly connected. These chemical parts will fail or degrade if not properly aligned, even if all the correct chemicals are present and light energy is available. These parts do not just snap into place. Each part is carefully constructed, checked for quality, transported to the correct location, inserted properly, and integrated by chaperone proteins.

This chemistry "found in nature" continues to provide examples of some of the most unlikely and unfavorable chemical reactions, but their production has been automated. Automated processes "feel like" they are easy, routine, highly probable, and spontaneous, so most people would call this natural. This is far from the chemical reality, and a more rigorous definition of "natural" is needed.

We need chemists, biochemists, molecular biologists, and physicists who continue researching the limits of spontaneous chemical reactions so that we can know what is possible with or without intelligence. Currently, the status quo in science is that any chemical system is possible given enough time and energy. However, the natural laws of chemistry and physics can only do so much on their own. Evidence built on decades of research shows how the elaborate nanoscale systems found in photosystems are far beyond the chemical reach of spontaneity. We are living in a time that allows a very detailed view of the incredible Intelligence that designed and implemented the unnatural chemical manufacturing system known as photosynthesis.

17

The Signature of the Creator Revealed in Photosynthesis

Susan Thomas

As students of science, we are impressed with the beauty and orderliness of creation. Personally, I have always been fascinated by the beauty, color, and intricate anatomy of leaves, recognizing in them the handiwork of the Master Designer.

Photosynthesis can be defined as the physicochemical process by which photosynthetic organisms use light energy to drive the synthesis of organic compounds.[1] The size, shape, color, thickness, and position of leaves on a plant are all significant for the process of photosynthesis. Various studies have shown that morphological and anatomical features of leaves as well as their orientation show a functional relationship with photosynthesis. For example, broad leaves tend to have larger petioles and veins and, hence, increased supply of water for photosynthesis, whereas thin laminar leaves reduce distance for diffusion of carbon dioxide and oxygen. Presence of a waxy cuticle and epidermal hairs affect the amount of sunlight absorbed, and plants in shady habitats show bicoloration, with sides of leaves not facing the sun lighter in color, enhancing the trapping of light.[2]

Under the microscope, we see in the epidermal layer of a leaf the symmetry of guard cells that make up the stomata that regulate the exchange of gases. Chloroplasts in the guard cells contain complex chlorophyll molecules essential for photosynthesis. It takes 17 enzymes to synthesize chlorophyll.[3] The lack of any one of these enzymes would prevent chlorophyll from being produced. Chlorophyll is responsible for the green color in plants and is made up of atoms arranged in a way that traps light energy.

The light-dependent stage of photosynthesis involves Photosystems I (P 700) and II (P 680), which are pigment molecules in the thylakoid membranes of chloroplasts. They are responsible for capturing photons of light energy and directing them to the reaction center for carbon fixation in what is known as photophosphorylation. The P 680 molecule is excited, and electrons are transferred to acceptors and down the electron transport system, losing energy in the process. This activates proton pumps in the thylakoid resulting in an H^+ gradient, causing the enzyme ATP synthase to produce adenosine triphosphate (ATP). In P 700 the primary acceptor is different, and electrons are transferred to nicotinamide adenine dinucleotide phosphate ($NADP^+$), which combines with an H^+ forming NADPH, which reduces CO_2 to glucose.

The light-independent reactions use this energy to reduce carbon dioxide to produce glucose in a process called the Calvin cycle. The three steps in the Calvin cycle are fixation, reduction, and regeneration. ATP from the light reaction is used to bind CO_2 to ribulose 1,5-biphosphate (RuBP). Phosphoglycerate with the help of NADPH gets reduced to phosphoglyceraldehyde, which regenerates RuBP. Plant cells that perform the light and dark reactions of photosynthesis produce six carbon molecules in just 30 seconds. This is a simple view of a complex process working in perfect harmony.[4]

Complex organic molecules are built from atmospheric carbon dioxide, and no matter how hard scientists have tried to replicate this technology in the laboratory, they have failed to match the ingenious machinery in plants. No incomplete intermediate system has been able to produce glucose or direct the precise enzymes required at each step. Could such a process have gradually developed with small changes by natural selection?

The 11 enzymes in the Calvin cycle perform their duties in sequential steps resulting in a number of intermediates in the process, and these, in effect, have no other metabolic function. If any of these enzymes were missing, the whole chain of reactions would be disrupted. Chance could result in cell destruction if only enzymes were present and substrates were not at the right place for enzymatic reactions. Based on the extensive knowledge that we have of this system, the statistical probability that these enzymes could have been produced to react with such precision in a stepwise evolutionary process over supposed millions of years is unfathomably small. Intelligent planning and design at the time of Creation would be essential to ensure that the complex process accurately accomplishes its purpose.

God programmed chloroplasts to convert sunlight into chemical energy in an orderly, assembly line fashion by the process of photosynthesis. However, what strikes me as even more amazing is that by manufacturing glucose, photosynthesis becomes essential to sustain animal life, because the breaking down of glucose to provide energy through respiration releases oxygen. This nonstop production, together with animal consumption of seeds, fruits, flowers, roots, and leaves, makes all complex metabolic activities in animals dependent on the energy produced by autotrophs. Ingenuity is accompanied by interdependence.[5]

This brief study of the miraculous manufacturing process of photosynthesis provides a glimpse of the Creator who cares about the incredible organization and every intricate detail of plants and their role within the biosphere. Let us not miss these scientific evidences of the majesty and greatness of our awesome Creator God.

18

A God of Law, Order, and Beauty

Mitch Menzmer

In the Bible we find a Creator God of law and order. He is also a God of beauty and wonder. Within the realm of Creation we find evidence of these attributes as well, a signature of His handiwork. Thermodynamics is one of many lenses through which we may observe the handiwork of God. Of thermodynamics, Albert Einstein said that it "is the only physical theory of universal content which, within the framework of the applicability of its basic concepts, I am convinced will never be overthrown."[1]

Within thermodynamics, there are three types of boundaries between a system and its surroundings: isolating, closed, and open. An isolating boundary permits no exchange of energy or matter and defines the first law of thermodynamics—that total energy within an isolated system is constant. A closed boundary permits exchange of energy with surroundings, but not matter, and an open boundary permits the exchange of both energy and matter with surroundings. If we choose a flower as a living system that exhibits beauty, we can establish rather easily that it represents an open boundary system. Its existence and function require both energy from the sun and matter in the form of water, carbon dioxide, and nutrients from the soil.

In addition to the first law, there is a second law in thermodynamics that is also crucial for the existence of our beautiful flower. This law is a statement about entropy, which has to do with the arrangement of matter and the dispersal of energy. A system with high entropy would be one in which energy is widely dispersed into various energy levels and locations, and one in which the arrangement of the material components of the system is highly non-specified. The highest entropy state available to a system exists in the equilibrium state. An equilibrium state is one in which, over time, there is no measurable change in energy at the macroscopic level (a good practical example would be a dead battery).

Perhaps the most significant aspect of the second law is its ability to predict the course of events—that there is a tendency in nature to drive all processes toward an equilibrium state. In other words, all spontaneous processes are eventually moving toward a state of equilibrium. However, due caution is required at this point. It is possible for the entropy of a subsystem within a larger isolated system to spontaneously decrease if there is an increase in entropy for the surroundings associated with the subsystem that at least counters the decrease in entropy gained by the subsystem.

Now that we have established the two basic laws of thermodynamics, let's look at how our beautiful flower is subject to them in its growth. The most freely available source of energy for our flower is heat from sunlight.[2] Per thermodynamics, heat is the flow of thermal energy that arises as the result of a temperature difference between two adjacent regions of space. There is great utility in being able to convert such an available source of energy into useful work.

Thermodynamics employs a model called a heat engine as a means of describing the process of conversion of heat into useful work. In this model, the engine is placed between two regions of differing temperatures so that energy can flow spontaneously (second law) from the region of high to low temperature, much as a grist mill is placed in a stream so that water may flow through and drive the grinding stones.

It is important to note that the production of useful work requires an engine consisting of very specified components performing very specified tasks, such as, in the case of the grist mill, the turning of a very specified set of wheels and gears so that proper grinding is accomplished. By the second law of thermodynamics, this would be a locally spontaneous decrease in entropy and a movement away from mechanical equilibrium. The "heat sink" in the case of the grist mill would be a low elevation area downstream of the mill, driving the continued flow of water.

In the case of a flower, the sun provides the input energy for the plant, and the useful work would be the manipulation of input molecules (water, carbon dioxide, nitrogen, and a few other nutrients) into highly specified arrangements that give rise to various processes of growth and reproduction. The work accomplished defines life for the plant—a state very low in entropy and thus far from equilibrium. The heat sink in the plant would be the chemical bonds in the molecules formed, often released as "carbs" in mammalian diet. The heart of the grist mill is the machinery that couples the flow of water to the mechanism responsible for accomplishing the very specific task of grinding grain. The heart of the flower is the DNA, which provides the information to construct the molecular machinery that directs how the input energy from the sun is to be coupled to the specific tasks of molecular arrangements. The net effect of these life-sustaining molecular arrangements does not exclude the existence of beauty in the form of the stem, leaves, and bloom of the flower.

It is well-recognized that there is something extraordinary about the properties of living systems, as expressed in a popular university-level text on biochemistry: "The collections of inanimate molecules that constitute living organisms interact to maintain and perpetuate life animated solely by the physical and chemical laws that govern the nonliving universe. Yet [these] organisms possess extraordinary attributes, properties that distinguish them from other collections of matter."[3] To me, the coupling of fundamental laws and sophisticated biomolecular machinery expressed in a beautiful flower speaks of the infinite wisdom of the Creator—that the laws found in creation not only permit but, in fact, ensure beauty.

PART IV

Filling the Waters and the Air

19

The Unseen Wonder of Coccolithophores

Emilia R. Belia

From beginning to end, the Bible presents a picture of God as actively involved in human history. To the Christian, the influence and power of God's Word to shape and transform the life of a single person, the dynamics of a community, the fate of a country, or the history of humankind is readily apparent. However, things become more complicated when trying to reconcile the current predominant scientific paradigm (naturalism) with the Scriptures.

In my own experience, the biblical account of Creation inspires and motivates me to look in nature for signs and clues about a Creator. Many can be found, whether at the macroscopic or microscopic level. For me, though, one of the most amazing things in this journey of discovery is unveiling the beauty and design of microscopic organisms. In this chapter we will explore the unseen wonder of microscopic algae known as coccolithophores and the extraordinary design and functions of their calcareous exoskeletons, which are the smallest skeletons in the marine world.

Living Coccolithophores

Coccolithophores are unicellular calcifying marine algae (haptophytes) characterized by the possession of a unique flagellum-like structure (haptonema). The function of the haptonema seems to be related to swimming, attachment, and capture of particles.[1] About 200 species of coccolithophores currently live in the oceans and are part of the plankton, which constitute 98% of the living biomass in the oceans. The remaining 2% comprises all the animals we can see macroscopically, like crabs, fish, and whales.[2]

Coccolithophores have an essential role in the global carbon cycle through photosynthesis and calcification. These algae reduce the amount of carbon dioxide (CO_2) in the atmosphere by converting CO_2, water (H_2O), and minerals into oxygen and organic matter and into calcium carbonate ($CaCO_3$) by calcification.[3] Coccolithophores and the rest of the phytoplankton form the basis of the marine food chain and are responsible for about half of the global primary production of oxygen, therefore being more important to our atmosphere than all of the earth's rainforests.

Haptophyte algae possess a tiny exoskeleton made of multiple scales. This exoskeleton (coccosphere) that covers the cell is made by an inner layer of organic body scales and an outer layer of minuscule calcite plates named coccoliths. Coccoliths (and organic scales) are secreted internally in the Golgi body and then extruded to the surface of the cell where they form the coccosphere[4] (see Figure 19-1A).

The Incredible Designs of Coccoliths

Coccolithophores produce diverse calcareous coccospheres of extraordinary designs. Although many other microalgae form exoskeletons of organic or inorganic scales, coccoliths are distinct and unique to the haptophytes.[5] Since coccolithophores possess remarkably small coccoliths, usually between 5 and 10 microns (0.005 and 0.01 mm) long, they are also called calcareous nannoplankton (less than 30 μm). Individual coccoliths and sometimes, under exceptional preservation, coccospheres can be found preserved in the fossil record. These tiny fossils are about the size of a human red blood cell.

Observation of coccolith morphology using scanning electron microscopy (SEM) and light microscopy reveals complex and multicyclic rim architectures (cycles of crystals). Broadly, coccoliths of living nannoplankton are built entirely of different submicroscopic calcite crystals organized in one or more radial cycles of circular to elliptical discs or rings (see Figure 19-1B). The morphologies of coccoliths are used for classification of species. In the fossil record, nannofossils also include coccoliths with uncertain biological affinities. This heterogeneous group shows some features of modern coccoliths including a wide range of shapes (e.g., star or rose, spindle, cylindrical, conical, pentagon).[6] One example within this group, *Braarudosphaera*, shows exceptional geometrical attributes, being characterized by pentagonal calcareous scales, called pentaliths, arranged in a regular pentagonal dodecahedron (see Figure 19-1C).

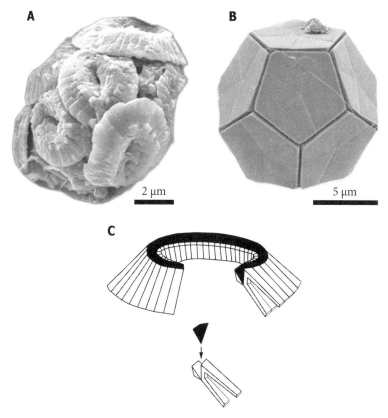

FIGURE 19-1. Examples of coccolith morphology. (A) Scanning electronic microscope (SEM) photograph of a coccosphere. (B) *Braarudosphaera sp.*, pentagonal-shaped coccolith. (C) General ultrastructure components of a coccolith.

Coccolith scales are thought to perform several functions for the organism, although no definitive use is agreed upon. Some of the suggested functions are related to protection, flotation, light regulation, and biochemical balance. Among these hypotheses, the one that captures my attention is the flotation or buoyancy function for the cell. The algae need to maintain their position within the photic zone to have access to sunlight and benefit from relative control over sinking and flotation. Imagine a person wearing a wingsuit falling from a high cliff and parachuting when approaching the land. The shape of the wingsuit and the parachute resembles the shape of coccoliths, and the fluid in our example would be air instead of water. The coccolith size and shape might give greater control over sinking rates.[7] This is just a simple aspect illustrating the importance of the design of coccoliths to coccolithophore ecology.

Conclusion

Beauty and design of microscopic organisms in association with functionality is not always appreciated in science. The design of coccoliths is important for the role of coccolithophores as a part of the marine ecosystem. Indeed, the functions of coccoliths are not limited to those mentioned above, and there is still much more to discover and understand. Yet, when I am looking at them with light or electron microscopes, I cannot help but admire their spectacular design. This combination of function and beauty reminds me of the infinite wisdom and power of God; it inspires me to join the psalmist's praise to our Creator, and declare: "Many, Lord my God, are the wonders you have done, the things you planned for us. None can compare with you; were I to speak and tell of your deeds, they would be too many to declare" (Ps. 40:5).

20

Foraging in the Ocean Twilight Zone

Christine Jackson

The largest of all toothed whales (Odontocetes) are the relatively elusive deep-diving sperm whales (*Physeter macrocephalus*), noted for their large conspicuous heads that measure one-third of their body length. These enormous whales can reach up to 20 m in length and 50,000 kg in weight. Their dives can exceed 1,000 m into oceanic waters in search of their preferred food source, squid. Sperm whales forage continuously day and night with diving times averaging 40 to 50 minutes although durations up to 138 minutes have been recorded.[1] Surface intervals of around 10 minutes between dives are used to release carbon dioxide and take in more oxygen. But how are these large marine mammals able to locate their prey in the dark ocean twilight zone, provide sufficient oxygen for their tissues, and survive the pressures and cold temperatures of the deep ocean?

A feature of all toothed whales is their capacity to use echolocation to find their prey.[2] Echolocation is the whale's ability to "see" by emitting specialized sounds to assess their environment and then listening to the sound waves as they rebound from distinctive objects or prey. "Monkey lips," or special valves, along with small fat bodies located in the upper nasal openings of the sperm whale's head are unique sound producers. Air is forced though the monkey lips, causing them to vibrate in a manner similar to human vocal chords. The sound, which is higher than frequencies heard by humans, is then directionally transmitted toward their prey by the spermaceti organ. This organ, which takes up much of the sperm whale's headspace, is filled with low-density lipids and acts as an acoustic lens. The short duration clicks produced as a result of this sound-production mechanism become more like a buzzing sound as the whale approaches its prey. Based on prey characteristics, sperm whales can change vibration frequency, interval, and duration to provide a three-dimensional image.

In sperm whales, sound is not directed into the middle ear through the ear canal as it is in humans but through highly sensitive fat tissue associated with the jaw. Sound is then conducted to the tympanic bulla in the inner ear. The tympanic bulla is suspended by connective tissue in a mixture of mucus, fat, and air that actually separates the middle ear from the skull and thereby focuses the sound waves to enhance reception. The fact that the membrane of the tympanic bulla is also reinforced with bony ligaments seems to likewise improve hearing of high frequencies.

Breath-holding sperm whales also have a number of physiological mechanisms to counteract compression and subsequent damage to tissues resulting from increasing hydrostatic pressure when diving at depth for prey.[3] The pressure within all the body's airspaces must match that of the ambient pressure so as to avoid any distortion or injury. With depth, the air-filled cranial sinuses become engorged, thus eliminating the air so as to prevent sinus squeeze. Moreover, the reinforcement of peripheral airways in sperm whales allows for a gradual collapse of the lungs with the air being pushed into the upper airways and stopping the exchange of gases in the blood. Limiting gas exchange is advantageous since it reduces nitrogen absorption and subsequently prevents nitrogen narcosis.

The lungs of sperm whales only store 5% of their total oxygen and are therefore not considered an important oxygen store. Instead the large volume of blood in sperm whales (200–260 mL/kg) acts as a substantial oxygen store.[4] Furthermore, much of the sperm whale's oxygen supply is due to elevated levels of the oxygen-binding proteins hemoglobin and myoglobin in the blood and muscles, respectively. Sperm whales can likewise reduce their oxygen use and energy consumption by slowing down their heart rate and metabolic rate when diving. Their streamlined and torpedo-like body along with extensive use of gliding provides minimal drag and reduced workload for the muscles, thus decreasing oxygen usage.

The ability to maintain body-core temperature (thermoregulation) is another essential physiological mechanism of the warm-blooded sperm whales, which forage in cold and extremely conductive waters. Their blubber (which may be as thick as 250 mm) aids in insulating the whale's organs.[5] Furthermore, their low body surface-to-volume ratio also reduces potential heat loss. An additional challenge sperm whales face is potential heat loss from their poorly insulated body appendages such as flukes and flippers, which contain limited blubber. To overcome this, they use a countercurrent system,[6] which involves arteries and veins that run in parallel but opposite directions. The cool incoming venous blood from the flukes and flippers that are exposed to the cold water is warmed by the outgoing arterial blood from the heart, forming an efficient heat-transfer mechanism. Conversely, when under heat stress, whales have a superficial venous system in their skin that is not warmed by outgoing arterial blood and thus enables the whale to cool down.

Sperm whales are amazingly designed for foraging and living in deep oceanic waters. The absence of any of the above interconnected mechanisms would affect their ability to survive in the hostile environment of the dark, deep, and cold mesopelagic zone. The ingenuity and integration of these efficient physiological systems speak to me of a wise Creator who took great care in implementing His designs.

21

Squid: Uniquely Adapted to a Changing Environment

George D. Jackson

I started studying tropical squids in Australia back in the 1980s. I was using what was then a fairly new technique of looking at statolith growth increments to age squid. Statoliths are essentially small calcareous "bones" in the squid head used to provide balance for swimming.

What interested me were the amazing regular rings or increments within the microstructure of the statoliths. My research was able to demonstrate that these rings were laid down daily and could thus be used as a powerful aging tool. Each squid essentially had a calendar in its head to indicate its age at capture and its growth rate. By conducting a number of laboratory experiments and then applying the aging technique to field populations, I was able to start understanding how tropical squid grow.[1] To my surprise, I discovered that these tropical species were all completing their life cycle in just a few months. This contrasted with the understanding at the time that these marine creatures lived for approximately five years or so. Considerable research since then has reconfirmed how these organisms live "life in the fast lane." Tropical species (including large reef squid) actually can complete their life span in less than 200 days, and it appears that many other temperate and cold-water species live for around a year.[2]

Squid show remarkable purpose in their complex biology. For example, they are designed to be able to dramatically adjust their rate of growth according to environmental conditions. Squid (especially tropical ones) are one of the fastest growing marine organisms, with incredibly rapid growth rates and short life spans. This raises the question as to how they achieve this. It turns out that they have a combination of unique features producing such fast growth rates. This includes rapid digestion and a protein-based metabolism, continual recruitment of new muscle fibers (hyperplasia), efficient oxygen utilization, and low levels of antioxidative defense.[3]

These features stand out in contrast to their fish competitors with which they share their ocean environment. Basically, a squid's metabolism is in high gear, with energy being used for growth rather than storage (squids don't seem to be able to use lipids as an energy store due to their protein-based metabolism). As a result, they grow rapidly and have short life spans. It is even possible that their efficient use of oxygen may be related to their mitochondria-rich fin musculature functioning independently of their circulatory system. This combination of design features means that squid display marked plasticity in growth. Simply being bigger doesn't mean that an individual is older. It depends on the environmental conditions an individual encountered while growing, with their unique design features allowing individuals to respond quickly when the environment changes.

The application of the ability to age individual squids provides us with a valuable means of exploring squid growth and maturity in varying environmental conditions. The small loliginid squid *Loligo opalescens* is found off the coast of California and has a life span of less than 260 days. Our team was able to follow cohorts of individuals through one of the most dramatic El Niño and La Niña events experienced in 1997–1998.[4]

During the El Niño conditions squids matured with a very small body size and had much slower growth rates. However, cohorts later during the La Niña event were much larger (e.g., comparing the El Niño summer of 1998 to the La Niña summer of 1999, males were 31% longer and 173% heavier, while females were 19% longer and 65% heavier, respectively). This was despite the fact that there was no clear trend in the ages of the cohorts. Virtually all the individuals were mature and the dramatic differences in body size were due to differences in individual growth rates rather than differences in life spans. There was also a significant positive correlation between mean monthly body size (grouped by hatching month) and the upwelling index determined for Southern California. So, the more upwelling occurring when a squid hatched, the larger the body size that individual reached at maturity.

This ecological study of *Loligo opalescens* demonstrated that they have a finely tuned set of physiological and biological qualities designed to adapt to the changing environmental conditions off the California coast. Greater upwelling during the La Niña produced a burst in productivity and greater food supply, resulting in faster growing individuals that achieved a larger size at maturity. This contrasted with the El Niño period of warmer temperatures, reduced upwelling, lower food supply, slower growth rates, and a smaller body size at maturity. In this way, they are acting as "ecosystem recorders and productivity integrators over time and space and are useful organisms to tie oceanography to biology."[5] This means that squid design includes a built-in ability to rapidly respond to favorable conditions, grow quickly, and reproduce in a very narrow window of time. This adaptability has resulted in an increase in squid and cephalopod populations generally as a result of overfishing of finfish.[6]

I personally see evidence of sophisticated design in the many complex facets of squid biology. Anatomy, metabolic, and physiological systems all work in concert to enable squid not only to survive but to thrive and adapt to rapidly changing oceanographic conditions. In reconciling these observations with my belief in a Creator God, I see this ability to respond and adjust as a manifestation of divine design.

22

Design in the Water-Salt Physiology of Fishes

Noble Donkor

In the study of animal physiology, we often seek to answer two central questions about how animals function: (1) what is the mechanism by which modern-day animals carry out their functions, and (2) why do modern-day animals possess the mechanisms they do? In this essay I describe how most biologists view the mechanism and origin of water-salt physiology of fishes and offer an alternative hypothesis to explain the same processes.

In terms of their water-salt physiology, aquatic animals confront challenges in maintaining a constant water and salt content of their bodies when they inhabit a range of environments on Earth—salt water, fresh water, salt lakes, glacial ponds, estuaries, etc. The body fluids of freshwater animals are more concentrated than the water in which they live. For example, in freshwater teleost (bony) fish, blood osmotic pressure averages about 300 milliosmolar (mOsm) higher than the osmotic pressure of freshwater, which is about 0.5–10 mOsm.[1] These fishes tend to gain water by osmosis and lose ions by diffusion, especially across permeable gill membranes, and in their urine. These passive fluxes of water and ions tend to dilute their body fluids. To void excess water, the kidneys of freshwater animals produce copious amounts of urine. For example, a goldfish might excrete urine equivalent to one-third of its body weight per day. The daily osmotic water influx of a goldfish will also equal one-third of its body weight. To replace lost ions, freshwater animals take up ions such as Na^+, Cl^-, and Ca^{2+} through active transport from their ambient water and food uptake.

On the other hand, the body fluids of marine fishes are far more diluted than the seawater in which they live. Such fish have blood osmotic pressure of approximately 300–500 mOsm, whereas the osmotic pressure of seawater is approximately 1,000 mOsm. Therefore, these fishes tend to lose water by osmosis and gain ions by diffusion. To replace water, they drink; however, to absorb H_2O from the seawater in their gut, they must actively take up NaCl, increasing their problem of salt loading. Their kidneys make urine that is approximately isosmotic to their blood plasma but is rich in divalent ions, and monovalent ions are excreted across the gills.[2]

These differences in environmental salinity require different designs in gill and kidney function.[3] For example, freshwater teleosts pump divalent cations out of the filtrate, while saltwater teleosts pump them in. The distal segment and collecting tubule are permeable in saltwater fish but impermeable in freshwater fish.

Most biologists describe these water-salt relations in fishes as an evolutionary vestige: their body fluids evolved as they adapted to their origins in the oceans, their later invasion to fresh waters, and re-invasion of the oceans millions of years ago.

Using the water-salt physiology of modern vertebrates, I offer an alternative interventionist hypothesis to suggest that marine and freshwater fishes were created with different designs for differing water salinities. Some species are designed to be able to adjust their gill and kidney function to enable them to move between environments with radically different salinities.

Anadromous fishes hatch in fresh water, migrate to marine water where they mature, and then return to fresh water to spawn. Depending on species, anadromous fishes spend one to several years at sea feeding and growing and then return to their natal stream where they breed. Salmon are an excellent example. These fishes are said to be euryhaline; they tolerate wide swings in salinity as they migrate between fresh and salt water. When these fishes swim into fresh water, the major physiological challenge is coping with salt loss across the gills. As euryhaline fishes pass part of their lives in fresh water and part in salt water, a period of adjustment usually involving several weeks (not millions of years) in brackish water is often required to allow acclimation. In such fishes, less gill activity occurs at isotonic environments than at low and high salinities.

Catadromous fishes, on the other hand, migrate in the opposite direction, from seawater to fresh water. They mature in streams and migrate to the ocean to breed. European and American eels are examples. Again, these fishes often require acclimation over a few weeks (not millions of years) to adjust.

Anadromous and catadromous fishes illustrate how the interventionist hypothesis of creation of fishes, living in streams and seas, and a subsequent global flood explains the data better than the hypothesis of gradual evolution. The interventionist model proposes that a design was already in place to permit them to survive in a variety of environments, because they could adapt to rapid changes in salinity, including those that may have occurred during the Flood.

If we believe that fish were created, they could have been designed with the genetic information to adapt to changing water conditions, possibly a requirement necessary to fulfill the mandate of filling the waters of the seas (Gen. 1:21–22). On the contrary, random processes seem utterly incapable of producing the molecular structures responsible for gill and kidney function in waters of differing salinity. I conclude that the manner in which fish regulate their water balance and internal ion concentrations points to an intelligent design.

23

Interrelated Design in the Swiftlet

Michael Tarburton

Birds have five main strategies for incubating eggs, and all five have been known for more than 150 years. It had been felt that every conceivable pattern for accomplishing the essential task of incubating the embryo in birds' eggs had been recorded. The basic categories are incubation by (1) both parents; (2) one parent only; (3) other adults of the same species; (4) other species (i.e., cuckoos); and (5) non-animal heat (e.g., megapodes using mounds of compost). However, in 1985 I discovered that Australian Swiftlets, which produce a clutch of one and cannot find enough food to feed two nestlings at the same time, are able to equal the annual productivity of other swiftlets such as the Fijian White-rumped Swiftlet, which produce clutches of two.[1] This is achieved despite the fact that both species can only find enough insect prey to raise their clutches for 125 and 150 days, respectively.

Australian Swiftlets employ an unexpected strategy: a second single-egg clutch is produced once the first nestling becomes homeothermic and is incubated by the first nestling. This strategy is so finely tuned that in most cases the second egg hatches the day after the first nestling fledges, allowing the parents to continue feeding the second nestling until it fledges just before the flush of insect prey reduces at the end of the wet season in the savanna environment.[2]

Another design feature is that most swiftlets have the ability to echolocate and find their way into the caves every night to sleep and to breed. I have found nests up to one kilometer from cave entrances in Samoa and Australia.[3] Nesting in caves reduces the number of predators that can end the lives of the adults or the nestlings, and swiftlets are designed with the ability to adapt their nesting behavior to their predators. In Fiji and Australia, they mostly nest high in the cave above a smooth area of roof or wall over which pythons cannot climb. In the Cook Islands, they spread their nests out inside the caves to avoid the two species of crabs that climb all over the cave walls, looking for nestlings to eat. In the highlands of Papua New Guinea, they nest on the floor of the cave as there are no ground-based predators.[4]

Swiftlets are able to build nests under the roof of caves because they are designed to make their nests out of their saliva. One species makes nests of pure saliva (nature's superglue), another places its own feathers in the nest, and most mix the saliva with Kangaroo Grass (in Australia), moss (Samoa), filmy ferns, and/or coconut fiber (Fiji). The only other birds that can echolocate are the oilbirds of South America, and in this God's creative ability and sense of humor are glimpsed, for oilbirds are vegetarians, feeding on oil palm fruit during the night and sleeping in caves during the day—the reverse timing of cave usage by swiftlets.

A third design feature is that swiftlets, like swifts, can fly all day without resting. Even during breeding, they hold the insects they catch in a pouch below their mouth that is designed to hold over 750 insects.[5] Their nestlings are designed to grow slowly, which means they can survive not only being fed just two or three times a day, but even during cyclones that prevent parents from catching food for several days.[6]

Why is it that swifts and swiftlets can fly all day? Work at Groningen University showed that their wings work quite differently from other birds. They use leading-edge vortices to provide lift.[7] Subsequent studies at the Lund University wind tunnel have shown some of the design features that enable low energy flight even while pursuing insects all day.[8] In swifts and swiftlets, the upstroke of the wing produces thrust as well as lift equal to 60% of the lift of the downstroke. Most birds do not produce any lift on their upstroke. Additionally, the lift/drag ratio was found to be the highest of any bird measured so far.

These advantages result from the stiffness of the feathers of the wing, the sweep of the wing, the tapered tip, as well as a changing wing shape. This wing design generates clockwise leading-edge vortices on the downstroke and anti-clockwise leading-edge vortices during the upstroke. All these elements together have the effect of increasing maneuverability in a bird that is otherwise designed for speed. This is a big help for a bird that feeds on flying insects.

Such a range of design features, all essential to enable swiftlets to do what they do, with none of them able to achieve their end results by themselves, speaks of an intelligent origin and a Creator who planned nature not only to achieve a multitude of diverse ecological relationships but also to occupy our minds for eternity.

24

Mathematics and Design in the Realm of Bees

Luciano González

Pappus of Alexandria (290–350 AD) was the last of the great Greek geometers. He is best known for his *Synagoge*, which is a voluminous collection of the most significant work done in ancient Greek mathematics. To him are attributed the following words that certainly frame the subject here exposed: "Bees … by a virtue of a certain geometrical forethought … know that the hexagon is greater than the square and the triangle and will hold more honey for the same expenditure of material."[1]

Tessellations, or tilings, are a collection of polygons that fill the plane with no overlaps or gaps. There are regular tessellations, those that use identical regular polygons to fill the plane, and semiregular tessellations that use two or more regular polygons, each with the same side length. There are only three regular polygons that can be used to tessellate the plane to form a regular tessellation: the equilateral triangle, the square, and the hexagon. This is possible because of the angle measures of these polygons. The angle around each vertex in a tessellation must be 360 degrees. Therefore, the interior angle degree of a regular polygon should divide into 360 evenly. The interior angles of the equilateral triangle, the square, and the hexagon are 60, 90, and 120, respectively, which fulfills the requirement. These are the only regular polygons with this property.

We share the planet with bees and appreciate these wonderful insects for their significant role in pollination and the production of honey and beeswax, among other things. However, when it comes to abstract thinking, bees are not known for formalizing theorems or writing manuals.

Clearly, bees have not studied the geometrical intricacies of tessellation theory or the principles of optimal construction design. Nevertheless, some of their behavior patterns when building a hive can be explained mathematically from the perspective of tessellation theory and optimal housing design. One such behavior that makes me think about God as the Creator and Universal Designer is the innate ability of bees to use the least expenditure of energy and materials.

Although the bees are surely unaware of the geometrical intricacies of tessellation theory, they were created with the ability to use the optimal design for their honeycombs. It can be mathematically demonstrated that of the three polygons, the hexagon has the smallest perimeter for a given area.[2] So, when bees are constructing hexagonal prism cells in the hive, they use less wax and do less work to enclose the same space than if tessellating space with prisms of square or triangular bases.[3] The honeycomb walls are made up of cells that are thirty-two hundredths centimeter thick, yet they can support 30 times their own weight.[4] The bees create hexagonal prisms in three rhombic sections, and the walls of the cell meet at exactly 120-degree angles.[5] What is truly remarkable is that bees work simultaneously on different sections of the honeycomb, which shows by their behavior a strong feeling of collectivity, communication, and unity of purpose throughout the hive.

I think God shows Himself in several ways in our universe, both in the animate and inanimate world. Particularly, through bees' behavior when building their honeycombs, we can think of God as an artist who loves order and beauty, since honeycombs are highly ordered and aesthetic structures. Beyond that, we can also ponder God as the mastermind who not only created bees as wonderful insects but also created us as His masterpiece. As such, we are called to observe critically our surroundings and understand how things work and how things are in the natural world. This understanding should eventually lead us to the acceptance of God as our Creator and Universal Designer.

PART V

Let the Earth Bring Forth

25

Phonotaxis:
The Meaningful Songs of Crickets

Benjamin Navia

If you have ever visited the countryside and taken a walk on a summer evening, you have most likely heard the sounds of crickets singing. These loud songs are acoustic pulses produced at specific frequencies and intensities that are meaningful and crucial for the reproduction and survival of these creatures.

Sound recognition in field crickets is rather complex and requires multiple steps that include cellular and molecular mechanisms. For instance, it requires activation of sensory receptors that tune to specific frequencies and intensities and activate higher-order neurons that provide excitatory or inhibitory input to other neurons in the prothoracic ganglion and brain of the animal. It also requires the release of specific neurotransmitters that relay action potentials across chemical synapses in nerve cells and specific receptor proteins, which are highly specific for such neurotransmitters. Ultimately, the decision of how the animal responds to the auditory signal is made in the brain, based on the information provided by auditory neurons and other local interneurons.[1]

Crickets have auditory receptors that can detect a wide range of sound frequencies. Their response to a particular auditory stimulus is indicated by whether or not they exhibit phonotaxis (i.e., the ability to move in relation to a source of sound). When female crickets are exposed to high frequency sounds, they walk away from the sound source. For these females, a high frequency sound represents a potential predator and so they exhibit negative phonotaxis.

However, in response to a lower frequency call (i.e., 4–5 kHz) the same animal will walk toward the sound source, exhibiting positive phonotaxis.[2]

How does the animal know to respond with positive phonotaxis to a given call? Several auditory neurons have been characterized in the cricket's brain and prothoracic ganglion, which are suspected to control phonotaxis.[3] For instance, the ascending neuron 2 (AN2; or L3 in the species *Acheta domesticus*), which is located in the prothoracic ganglion and projects axons to the brain, is very sensitive to both 16 and 5 kHz calls.

Calls are repetitions of chirps, with each chirp containing three to four pulses of sound, called syllables. Electrophysiological recordings show that in response to 16 kHz calls, the L3 neuron produces a burst of action potentials to every single syllable of the chirp. Similar recordings show that when exposed to 5 kHz calls, the L3 not only responds with fewer action potentials overall to the lower frequency stimulus, but it also shows a decrease in the number of action potentials produced to consecutive syllables of the chirp in response to attractive calls. By manipulating the syllable period within a chirp, the calls can be made less attractive, which results in an unexpected increase in the number of L3's action potentials. Based on this evidence, timing seems to be of utmost importance to the attractiveness of the call.[4]

The L3 neuron is just one element of a network of neurons responsible for identifying attractive calls. The fact that L3 exhibits different response patterns to 5 kHz versus 16 kHz signals indicates that various elements of the network that connect with L3 are being recruited in the response to the acoustic stimulus.[5] Such elements are providing unique information to L3, which seems to combine it and send its output to the brain for further processing. The correlation between the response of the L3 neuron to acoustic stimuli and the movement observed in the individual under study allows us to continue to investigate the underlying neural mechanisms that control phonotactic behavior in crickets.

However, a brief and partial description of how a single auditory neuron in a female cricket both responds to different stimuli and parallels phonotaxis is far from being the complete story. Additional factors such as the age of the animal, neuromodulators, hormones, and environmental temperature can further influence the neuronal and behavioral response of the animal, as can many other neurons that are involved in recognition and control of phonotaxis in the nervous system of these creatures. All of this contributes to the complexity of a recognition system that was once thought to be fixed and simple but has since been demonstrated to exhibit considerable variability as we continue to learn more about how networks of neurons control behavior. Moreover, if we think of acoustic communication between sender and receiver as a story, then reception of the signal and processing by the receiver constitute just one chapter. Additional separate chapters include production of the signal and the properties of the medium through which the sound signal travels.

It certainly requires a mastermind to design such a complex system with elements that exhibit precise tuning while allowing for variability and plasticity of the system. The alternative view is that random, undirected processes equipped an organism with key molecular elements (not discussed in this essay) required for proper functioning. Chance also provided individual neurons with intrinsic properties, such as the ability to tune to specific frequencies and integrate multiple inputs, and organized networks of neurons in ways that would allow the organism to recognize attractive from unattractive calls leading to a specific behavior. The more we learn about the details of this recognition system, the greater the conviction that randomness cannot produce such complexity and organization of life, and this only makes sense in light of an intelligent Designer.

26

Design, Spiders, and "Integrated Wholes"

David R. Nelsen

As someone who is willing to consider design as a legitimate aspect of nature, how I view the natural world can be very different from many of my scientist friends and colleagues. They believe in metaphysical naturalism: all that exists in the universe is matter and energy which, combined with the fundamental laws of physics, are sufficient to explain the universe, the earth, and the diversity of life on Earth. Metaphysical naturalism assumes that simple materials and processes can produce higher-order complexity—that is, the universe grew out of simpler starting materials. However, this assumption is antithetical to the major assumption of those of us who consider design as an explanation. Design requires that some other entity exists who is responsible for that design. The existence of this entity means complexity existed from the beginning. Thus, considering design as an explanation leads to a very different view of the world.

As I work within and evaluate the design paradigm, I am struck by how well-honed organisms are. They are composed of many different interacting parts that form complex systems. Often, these systems are integrated with other systems, culminating in the entire organism. Such organisms are what I call "integrated wholes." All major general biology textbooks begin by presenting the chemical and physical processes that govern life, then build on these processes to discuss molecular and cellular biology, followed by anatomy and physiology, and end with ecology.

As I have taught from these textbooks, two things have occurred to me. First, at every level, I continuously see the theme of "integrated wholes." From the function of a single cell to the balance within an ecosystem, I see integrated wholes becoming part of larger integrated wholes. Second, the textbooks fail to emphasize the idea of integrated wholes, and instead favor a reductionist approach in an effort to support the evolutionary connectivity of life. The authors are preoccupied with explaining the origin of structures or processes, produced by the lucky accumulation/modification of existing parts, but they do not consider the level of integration necessary for these structures or processes to exist. It is like explaining the shape and function of a gear in a clock, without considering the function of the clock as a whole. Even if we understood all of the parts that make up a structure or process, this is often insufficient for understanding the entire process itself as the whole is greater than the sum of its parts. I believe that design leads us to see and appreciate this aspect of nature far more clearly than metaphysical naturalism does.

To illustrate more fully what I mean by "integrated wholes," I will use one of my favorite groups of animals: spiders. Spiders are one of eleven orders of arachnids, at least six of which are known to possess chemical systems used in either predation, defense, or both. The most current phylogenetic analysis,[1] in conjunction with their unique anatomical features, suggests that these chemical systems likely originated independently at least five times. Spiders are unique among arachnids in possessing and using silk. Simply saying that spiders have silk does not do this amazing ability justice. In fact, spiders have up to eight different silk glands,[2] each capable of producing a unique type of silk. Almost every structure a spider makes from silk is composed of many of these separate silk sub-types. Spider venom is even more complex, being composed of hundreds to even thousands of proteins, peptides, amines, and other components.[3]

Nevertheless, it does not end there; venom and silk can only do their work when they are combined with the other amazingly complex systems within spiders. For example, spiders acquire information about their environment through numerous specialized sensory organs (lyriform organs, tricobothria, chemosensory hairs) located on the outside of their body. These weird and wonderful sensory organs must in turn be integrated with the hydraulic muscular system via the nervous system.

My point is that every behavior is the outcome of the sophisticated integration among all of the spider's individual systems. The fact that a spider can choose to inject venom and, if it chooses to inject venom, control the amount of venom injected is astonishing.[4] What makes a spider a spider is the completeness of this integration, and this integration cannot be reduced without losing the essence of what it means to be a spider. Even though at some level none of the individual parts that a spider possesses is unique, no other organism integrates all of these parts the way spiders do. No other organism even comes close. What it means to be a spider is more than just an individual part; it is the summation of all those parts combined.

Because I allow myself to consider design as a driving force in nature, I see the world differently. Design leads me to consider not only the individual parts of an organism or process but also the interaction of those parts and the summation of those interactions that make up the whole. It leads me to think of organisms not only from the bottom up but from the top down, the inside out, and every other direction. A pluralistic approach alone will enable us to understand and model how "wholes" work.[5] The entirety of the whole is more important than any of the individual parts.

27

Spider Silk: Design at All Levels

Rivelino Montenegro

Despite all the improvements in science, our solar cells are still extremely inefficient, our medical implants are far from perfect, and our buildings need serious improvement. Where can we find ideas to solve such engineering problems?

Scientists, like poets and painters, have repeatedly turned to nature to search for inspiration since everything in it seems to provide the best outcome with the lowest waste of energy. We call this sort of work biomimetics, or finding inspiration and drawing solutions from nature.

An evolutionist, although not believing that nature has had any design or purpose in mind, will explain this close-to-perfect state of the natural systems as being due to the fact that nature had millions of years to try, improve, and perfect its own mechanisms.

If you read any book about biomimetics, you may be surprised to find that no matter how strongly the author believes in Darwinian evolution, he or she cannot find a better word than "design" to describe nature's solutions. The word "design" will be used in the textbooks, leading inevitably to the search for a designer.

Spider silk is one of the most fascinating natural structures. Scientists are impressed not only by its structural properties and chemical composition but also by the way spiders control its synthesis.

More than 15 years ago, I wrote a short essay[1] about the design behind the spiderweb and the fascinating material of which it is constituted. The mystery and fascination surrounding this material persist, given its immense potential engineering applications.

Material scientists have been dreaming about a material that would be highly elastic, while stronger than steel and at the same time much lighter. Spider silks are among the strongest and toughest fibers known to science.[2] Using a diverse array of proteins, spiders are able to construct silk fibers that vary tremendously in their mechanical properties, ranging from major ampullate silk with a tensile strength rivaling that of steel to flagelliform silk with a stretchiness approaching that of rubber. A single spider can produce up to seven different types of silk for different uses.[3]

Interestingly, spiders not only know how to change the chemistry of their silk but also the diameter of the thread. Since spiders can dramatically change their own weight and size, they can actively control the diameters of silk threads spun under different environmental conditions, increasing the load-bearing capacity of their draglines.[4]

However, the fundamental question about spider silk is not just the physical-chemical basis of its fascinating properties, but the origin of a sophisticated silk synthesizer inside spiders, able to fine-tune the desired silk composition and thickness for a variety of applications, including hunting, sheltering, and even flying, or, more precisely, ballooning.[5]

Spiders can be found everywhere in different sizes, colors, and shapes, but all of them have one thing in common: they can produce silk. Similar to the egg and hen question, we have to find an answer as to what came first. Silk is crucial for the survival of the spider. How then, from an evolutionary point of view, did spiders get the ability to produce silk?

Analysis of DNA sequences coding for the C-terminus—also known as the carboxyl-terminus or COOH-terminus—of spider silk proteins from a range of spiders shows a high level of similarity, which is usually interpreted to suggest that many silk C-termini share a common origin and that their physical properties have been highly conserved.[6]

Similarities among different spider silk genes may suggest that they share a common ancestor, but the evolutionary relationships among functional homologues are unclear. It is thought that many of the genes in this family have evolved through gene duplications. Functional relationships are further complicated by the existence of duplicate silk glands, spigots, and spinnerets.[7]

Evolutionists do not have an answer for the origin of spider silk. Silk spinnerets are not found in any postulated evolutionary ancestor, but are only found in certain insects and in spiders, including a Triassic fossil.[8] Different types of spiders have similar silk proteins that have a wide range of physical properties. The degree of similarity among physical properties and predicted secondary structure of silk C-termini suggests that they perform a common function and that changes are likely to be constrained by selection against mutations that disrupt this function.

The very complex and intelligent way spiders control the chemistry of their silk for each specific application, the way spiders determine the diameter of the thread and the geometry of the web, and the fact that such intricate abilities and mechanisms have appeared together in spiders since the beginning of their fossil record supports the idea of a Designer instead of Darwinian evolution.

28

Extreme Plasticity in the Skull Shape of Dogs

Rebecca J. Greer

The extreme skull shape differences in the *Canis familiaris* (domestic dog; see Figure 28-1) have been postulated as an example of evolution since Darwin wrote *On the Origin of Species*. Shapes and sizes range from the small, brachiocephalic (short-faced) Pekingese breed that can weigh as little as 2.5 kg to the larger dolicephalic (long-faced) Borzoi breed that can weigh up to 45+ kg, with multiple variations in between. These variations among the domestic dog are greater than the variation of skull shapes across the order Carnivora[1] and have been documented to occur in short time periods. For example, historical records of purebred St. Bernards were evaluated over 120 years and found to have undergone considerable morphological transformation.[2]

It has been suggested that the absence of survival pressures on dogs and their selective breeding and feeding have allowed all the different shapes to occur,[3] as some breeds would not survive without human protection/selection. Take for example the English Bulldog. Under most circumstances, the reproduction of the purebred English Bulldog is controlled by humans. The female is artificially inseminated because she cannot hold up the weight of the male during live breeding, and the pups are delivered by Cesarean section as the pelvic canal is too narrow for natural birth of the large-shouldered offspring.

The extreme changes in the bulldog result in brachiocephalic airway disease in which the soft palate is elongated and can drop into the upper larynx causing airway obstruction, with the nares having a decreased diameter resulting in reduced air flow and increased airway pressure. These changes in the airway result in numerous clinical problems including noisy breathing (stertor), exercise intolerance, heat intolerance, and difficult breathing (dyspnea). Associated with the brachiocephalic syndrome are other diseases such as fainting (syncope), gastrointestinal disease, increased prevalence of cancer, and obesity. These clinical diseases make it unlikely a bulldog could survive without human protection in the form of food provision (too aerobically challenged to chase down prey), protection from heat (most cannot tolerate temperatures above 30°C), and reproductive assistance. The selection of traits has resulted in reduced vigor and viability to the English Bulldog (the antithesis of evolution) but has not resulted in the bulldog becoming something other than a dog.

The evolutionary narrative purports that the plasticity of the dog skull is due to removal of the selective pressure of wild survival. But even in the absence of those constraints and in the presence of the

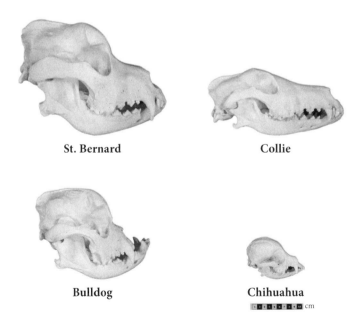

FIGURE 28-1. Examples of diversity in the shape of dog skulls.

most extreme breeding changes that can be implemented by humans, a domestic dog remains a dog.

Some see these observations on skull variability to uphold evolution, but I see them as examples of design. For example, a word processing program allows books, pamphlets, letters, and various other documents to be produced with very different formats and layouts; but no matter how much the settings are adjusted, a word processing program does not become a video game. The domestic dog (or potentially the entire *Canis* group) was designed in a similar fashion. Many different shapes and size potentials are in the system such that the skulls of various dogs may not even appear to be in the same order of animals and yet it remains *Canis domesticus*. The system was designed with such great variability that a domestic dog can be bred to have a long nose or a short one, upward or downward facing nose, a large or small head, long or short body and legs, or other variations. The original design is such that the domestic dog can assist humans in many capacities and forms, yet it is still a dog and by breeding cannot be made into another kind of animal.

The extreme changes in a domestic dog's skull and overall conformation also give rise to another interesting thought relating to the fossil record. In many cases, we only have fossils to tell us of an extinct species or animal. No DNA or other data is available to make decisions about what species or group that fossil may fit into. If we did not already know the plasticity of a dog skull and found a fossil skull of both a Pekingese and a Borzoi, or a Chihuahua and a Greyhound, or any other very different dog breeds, we would be unlikely to consider the two fossils as individuals of the same species, or able to interbreed. This is an example of the limits of information that can be gathered from the fossil record.

Humans have pushed selection to the extreme in the various domestic dog breeds, yet they have been unable to create any species other than the domestic dog, an indication that different kinds of animals are not the result of evolution, but were created originally, as described in Genesis 1:24.

PART VI

In God's Image

29

Our Spectacular Skeletons

Liliana Endo-Munoz

Our bones are not just rigid structures made up of collagen and minerals but are living and dynamic organs that grow, change shape, and regenerate themselves throughout our lives through a process called "bone remodeling." This process involves development, maintenance, repair, and growth and depends on the complex and tightly controlled activity of two major cells—osteoblasts (OB), which make new bone, and osteoclasts (OC), which resorb or break down bone. Both cell types work with opposing functions, with timely precision, and in perfect balance. Their activity is controlled by cartilage-making cells; by osteocytes, which are cells embedded in the bone mineralized matrix; and by an extensive regulatory network of genes and signaling pathways.

These complex multistep pathways are driven by a vast array of active proteins, each of which is explicitly coded by DNA for a specific purpose. Each step in a signaling pathway involves several of these proteins working in a synchronized and hierarchical manner. The entire process of bone remodeling is tightly regulated at the level of DNA through a variety of chemical changes in the DNA molecule.[1] In turn, DNA is tightly regulated by numerous short non-coding RNA molecules called microRNA.

OC and OB derive from different types of stem cells and follow two independent, multistep processes of development before reaching maturity and full activity. Both processes need to coexist and function simultaneously in a coupled manner to keep a balance between bone formation and resorption. If one exceeds the other, formation and maintenance of a healthy and well-functioning skeleton does not occur.

Multitasking Bone Cells

OB originate primarily from a subset of mesenchymal stem cells (MSC) which, depending on signaling, can also develop into cartilage, muscle, or fat cells. Once OB reach maturity, they secrete new bone. In addition, a fraction of mature OB become embedded in the bone matrix as osteocytes, which release proteins that are critical for the regulation of bone remodeling.[2]

OC are giant cells containing not just one, but multiple nuclei. Unlike OB, they originate from hematopoietic stem cells (HSC).[3] Depending on signaling, HSC can develop into at least 12 different types of white blood cells. One of these, the monocyte, can remain a monocyte or develop into either of two immune cells—dendritic cells or macrophages. Macrophages can either remain as they are or develop into OC through the combined action of several proteins in a multistep process facilitated by OB and osteocytes.[4] Therefore, preexisting functional OB and osteocytes are required for the development of fully functional OC.

Once mature, OC create a "bone resorption pit" through a complex process in which the cell secretes hydrogen ions that break down bone matrix minerals and enzymes that break down collagen and generate reactive oxygen species. As the bone matrix is broken down, it releases several proteins. These, together with OC, help to recruit immature OB to the "construction site" and also push their development into mature cells that secrete new bone to fill the resorption pit.[5] Therefore, preexisting functional OC are required for the development and full functionality of OB.

Interestingly, the stem cells (MSC and HSC) that give rise to OB and OC, both reside in the bone marrow that fills the cavity inside bones. In addition, the OC plays a major role in the establishment and maintenance of the HSC niche from which it itself derives.[6] In other words, preexisting, fully functional bone is required for the development of fully functional bone.

Bone cells also play multifunctional regulatory roles outside the skeleton.[7] For example, OB influence the function of blood vessels and cells of the central nervous system, gut, muscle, fat, and testis, while OC have effects on the hematopoietic (blood cells) and immune systems.[8]

Imbalance and Catastrophe

The balance between bone formation and resorption is achieved through multiple mechanisms that involve bone cells, immune cells, and numerous functional proteins, all of which can respond quickly to varying stimuli. The astounding complexity of these mechanisms indicates that for bone development and remodeling to occur successfully, all independent processes and cells must codevelop and coexist to synchronize and synergize in a balanced and coupled manner.

The entire process is so tightly regulated that any disruption results in an imbalance between bone formation and resorption, leading to catastrophic events that cause disease and mortality. The most common of these is osteoporosis, where bone resorption exceeds formation, leading to decreased bone density and fractures.[9] Uncontrolled OC activation contributes to inflammatory arthritis and to painful bone-resorbing tumors that spread to the skeleton from common cancers such as breast, prostate, or melanoma. Our own research[10] has shown that OC play a major role in osteosarcoma, an aggressive juvenile bone cancer. A recent finding shows that alterations in bone cells can lead to the development of leukemia stem cells. On the other hand, genetic mutations that inhibit OC formation or function lead to the accumulation of dense but brittle bone in rare disorders such as osteopetrosis.[11]

Design or Evolution?

This brief synopsis of a mechanism that is exceedingly much more intricate argues in favor of the simultaneous existence of numerous established and interdependent regulatory proteins and pathways, working with synergistic precision to facilitate the formation and maintenance of a functioning organ. Such observed complexity and codependence challenge an evolutionary model of stepwise and slow bone development over millions of years. Instead, the evidence highlights the need for a rapid, responsive, highly complex, tightly regulated, and coupled design with high plasticity, which is sensitive to the slightest imbalance and which not only influences its immediate environment, but coregulates the entire organism. We are only scratching the surface of this multifaceted process, and I look forward to spending eternity with the Designer to learn the rest of the story.

30

The Amazing Gift of Hearing

Lucinda Hill Spencer

Have you ever considered what life would be like in this world without sound? No music, no birdsongs, no sounds of laughter or the voices of our loved ones. No warnings of danger from a train whistle or the barking of a dog. Those who struggle with a hearing impairment have perhaps a deeper understanding of the importance and value of the gift of sound. But have you ever wondered what gives someone the ability to hear the familiar sounds of life? The design of the structures and mechanisms required for hearing is truly amazing.[1]

Sound is a vibration that is transmitted through air, liquids, and solids. These vibrations, or sound waves, occur at different amplitudes and frequencies. The amplitude of the sound wave relates to the volume of the sound. Sound waves for loud sounds have a higher amplitude, while soft sounds come from sound waves with a lower amplitude.

Sound wave frequency relates to the pitch. A rapid rate of vibration, or high frequency sound wave, results in a high-pitched sound. A low frequency sound wave has a slower rate of vibration and results in a low-pitched sound.

The external ear is designed to funnel sound waves to the tympanic membrane, or eardrum, which then vibrates at the same frequency as the sound wave. In the middle ear, three tiny bones, called ossicles, transmit these vibrations from the eardrum to the cochlea, which is in the inner ear.

The cochlea is shaped like a snail shell and is filled with a fluid called perilymph. This spiral-shaped tube contains a smaller tube called the cochlear duct, like the inner tube of a bicycle tire. The cochlear duct is formed by two membranes—the basilar membrane and the vestibular membrane—and also contains fluid, called endolymph.

When vibrations from the eardrum are transmitted to the cochlea, it causes waves in the perilymph and endolymph. These waves cause distortions of the basilar membrane of the cochlear duct. Different tones cause distortions in different areas of this membrane. High-pitched tones cause distortions of the basilar membrane near the base of the spiral-shaped cochlea, while low-pitched tones cause distortions near the apex.

The cochlear duct contains some intricate structures. Hair cells on the basilar membrane have tiny hair-like protrusions, called microvilli, at one end. These microvilli touch another membrane, the tectorial membrane, which is stationary. As the basilar membrane moves with the sound vibrations, the microvilli bend. This transmits a signal to a nearby nerve cell, which in turn transmits a signal to the auditory portion of the brain.

The mechanism through which these signals are transmitted is fascinating. When the microvilli of a hair cell bend in a certain direction, they pull on tiny springs that are attached to the gates of potassium channels. This causes the gated potassium channels to open so that potassium ions can pour into the cell from the surrounding fluid. This changes the electrical charge within the hair cell, causing voltage-gated calcium channels to open.

As calcium ions pour into the hair cell, the electrical charge within the cell changes even more. This causes an increased release of neurotransmitters from the hair cell. These neurotransmitters act on nearby nerve cells, which then send electrical signals called action potentials to the brain.

The change in the electrical charge of the hair cell also opens voltage-gated potassium channels, causing potassium ions to leave the cell so it will be ready to start the process all over again.

Now let's consider what happens in the brain so that we can perceive sounds from the world around us. The action potentials that are generated in the cochlea are transmitted through the auditory nerve pathways to the part of the brain known as the auditory cortex. These nerve pathways are complex with many different connections.

Action potentials that are generated near the base of the cochlea stimulate nerve cells in a specific part of the auditory cortex. These nerve cells, or neurons, interpret the electrical signals as a high frequency, or high-pitched sound. Other action potentials generated near the apex of the cochlea stimulate different neurons, which interpret them as a low frequency or low-pitched sound.

Many of the sounds that we hear are very complex. We are able to recognize different voice qualities or the distinctive sounds of a violin, trumpet, or flute. We can simultaneously hear combinations of many sounds, like the exquisite music of a symphony orchestra. We can even distinguish the direction from which a sound is heard and focus on the sounds most important to us, like a mother tuning in to her child's voice.

We can also perceive the volume of the sound. High-amplitude sound waves from loud sounds cause greater vibration of fluid in the cochlea and of the basilar membrane, which results in more intense stimulation of the hair cells. This causes more frequent action potentials to be transmitted to the auditory cortex, which is interpreted as a louder sound.

The design of the ear and cochlea is truly amazing, but without the auditory nerves and cortex we would still be unable to hear the sounds around us or understand what they mean. How the brain interprets the electrical signals from the cochlea as noise, beautiful music, or the familiar voices of our loved ones is a mystery we have barely begun to explore.[2]

If any part of this amazing system does not work properly, we are unable to hear. The eardrum and ossicles must be able to transmit sound waves to the cochlea. The fluid, membranes, and hair cells of the cochlea must function properly in order to open the potassium and calcium channels and generate action potentials.[3] The auditory nerve pathways must be intact and the auditory cortex of the brain must function normally in order for us to perceive and understand the sound waves that surround us.

The gift of hearing is the result of an integrated system of complex structures that work in coordination to transmit signals to the brain. These signals are then processed to give meaningful sensory input that is valuable for our lives. The intricate design required for this amazing gift speaks to us of a Designer and suggests that this Designer is an audiophile who understands the importance of sound and hearing for our happiness.

31

The Human Eye: Designed for Vision

Jesson Martin

The human eye is a fascinating example of optical and anatomical design.[1] Human vision has significant functional contributions ranging from tear film, cornea, lenticular optics, aqueous and vitreous humor, pupil, and retinal layers. Vision is possible due to the interaction of light with the optics of the eye and the efficient way an image is transferred to the retina, converted into information, and transmitted to the processing centers in the brain. At each component of the eye (tear film, cornea, iris, crystalline lens, and retina), there is less room for error for it to function efficiently. In this short essay I will describe some aspects of the eye design that give human vision its great accuracy and precision. The more I consider these aspects, the more I become convinced that we were indeed "fearfully and wonderfully made" (Ps. 139:14).

Tear Film

The most anterior refractive surface of the human eye is the pre-corneal tear film, which is only about 4 μm thick and has a refractive index of 1.34. The tear film lipid layer provides a smooth optical surface for the cornea that is vital for eye comfort and visual performance. After every blink, the tear film spreads over the cornea within one second and remains there for about four seconds. After five seconds, the ocular surface will start to experience tear breakup due to evaporation of the aqueous component of tears. If the eye doesn't blink within about five seconds, tear film breakup will start to seriously degrade the image quality due to the large change in refractive index at the air–tear interface.

Corneal Transparency

The cornea contributes about two-thirds of the total optical power of the human eye (about 60 diopters). It consists of 80% stroma (fibers), which are filled with collagen fibrils about 30 nm in diameter with a spacing of 65 nm. The precise spacing of collagen fibrils produces a regularly arranged matrix that allows light to pass through without experiencing diffraction effects, thereby making the cornea transparent. A slight change in the spacing of the fibrils would cause the cornea to become opaque due to destructive interference of the light.

Lens Refractive Power

The crystalline lens contributes about one-third of the total static optical power of the eye. The lens helps in image formation on the retina and importantly provides for focusing at different target distances (accommodation). The lens has a biconvex form with its anterior surface over 1.5 times larger than the posterior surface. It has a thickness of about 3.6 mm (relaxed eye) and a diameter of about 9 mm. The crystalline lens is avascular and has no pigments. Thus, it absorbs little light, transmitting most of it to the retina. The refractive index (RI) of the crystalline lens varies radially from being largest at the center with an RI of 1.402 to smallest at the edge with an RI of 1.375. Such gradient index (GRIN) lenses are extremely difficult to manufacture or to find commercially available. Nevertheless, they are very commonly seen in nature, despite the specificity and complexity of the design. If humans were to possess a single refractive index lens instead of a GRIN one, we would be missing about eight diopters of optical power.

Duplex Retina

"The greater light to govern the day and the lesser light to govern the night" (Gen. 1:16). This statement fits well with the function of the retina. Based on the retinal architecture one could say "cone photoreceptors for day and rod photoreceptors for night." The photopic (day vision) spectral sensitivity or luminous efficiency is about 550 nm, and scotopic (night vision) spectral sensitivity is about 507 nm. Our visual system shifts the peak sensitivity from day vision (550 nm) to night vision (507 nm), an adjustment called the Purkinje shift.

The retina contains about six million cones with a maximum at the fovea. The foveal pit, which is responsible for providing sharp central vision, is about thirty-five hundredths of a millimeter wide and is in the macular region of the retina. Cones are avascular, allowing for light to pass through without any loss. The cone system has exceptionally high spatial and temporal resolution due to the packing density of the receptors and their one-to-one connection with the ganglion cells in the fovea. The photopic (cones) system has superior chromatic and contrast sensitivity. On the other hand, there are about 120 million rod photoreceptors, and they are not present in the fovea. The rod photoreceptors are highly sensitive in dim light. The rod photoreceptor system plays a vital role in human night (scotopic) vision. This system has great ability to sum up signals (at ganglion cells) from multiple rod photoreceptors to achieve high sensitivity (spatial and temporal summation). For this reason, the absolute luminous efficiency of scotopic vision is three times higher than the photopic vision.

Retinal Adaptational Range

The luminance adaptational range of the human eye is from 10^{10} (sun) to 10^{-6} (light threshold/starlight) candelas/m^2. The eye can adjust to about 10 billion units of retinal luminance, of which only one billion units are accounted for by the pupillary ability (dilation and constriction). The remainder is contributed by the retinal layers, especially the photoreceptors.

Functional Retina

The retina also includes horizontal cells, bipolar cells, amacrine cells, and ganglion cells. Without these cells, we would not be able to resolve fine details, leaving us with blurry images, lack of light modulation, inaccurate motion detection, and other perceptual challenges. Each retinal layer is vital for our visual performance.

If you look at the retinal architecture, it may seem counterintuitively arranged backward. The photoreceptor is located at the back of the retina next to the retinal pigment epithelium (RPE). This architecture is imperative as RPE replenishes nutrients to the receptor cells, absorbs light that was not absorbed by the photoreceptors, and keeps blood-borne pathogens from infecting the eye. So, after all, it is not backward, but cleverly designed.

32

Why Chimpanzees Can't Play Chopin

David G. Pennington

Having spent 40 years in the practice of surgery, much of that performing microsurgery,[1] I have often pondered the amazing structure of the human body that allowed the fine patterns of dexterity that produced the *Mona Lisa*, carvings of Chinese ivory figures, elaborately illuminated Bibles of medieval times, the hand assembly of microprocessors, and many other intricate works. This ability to perform manual tasks involving fine movement differentiates the human from all other primates. Accomplishments such as the concert performance of Chopin's Etude in G# minor, op. 25, no. 6, or the performance of brain surgery are a universe beyond the technical ability of even the smartest ape.

Currently, presupposed concepts based in evolutionary biology dominate the field of human neurophysiology. The cognitive advantage of the human brain has been attributed to its large size,[2] in particular encephalo-cortical mass, which is genetically controlled. A gene, strangely called "microcephalin," regulates human brain size.[3,4] The large functional representation occupied by the human hand, especially the thumb and index finger in the parietal lobe cortical areas, adds adjunctive support to this concept but does not explain why it happens.

Furthermore, the functional anatomy of the human hand is designed for precise movements that are impossible for other primates. The longer and fully opposable thumb of the human is the chief example, producing the "pincer" or pen-grip used in art, writing, surgery, etc., something not possible for the chimpanzee.[5] The

independent complex movement of fingers required for piano play-
ing and other dexterous activities enjoyed by humans is not seen
among apes, nor is it required for their daily existence. There is no
evolutionary advantage to the appreciation of Beethoven's Fifth, let
alone the ability to play it.

The sensory end-organ density of human fingertips partly
explains its large representation on the post-central parietal cortex of
the brain. Sensory discrimination is at least as important as motor
function in the performance of fine movement, as is the rapid feed-
back of position and stretch receptors in muscles and joints, rapidly
informing the brain, especially the cerebellum, of exact spatial positioning, accurate to fractions of a millimeter in some cases.

The world of neuroanatomy was recently updated in an amazing
way when in late 2018 the Australian neuroanatomist, Professor
George Paxinos, announced the discovery of a new cerebral nucleus
at the base of the human brain.[6] Paxinos, a world leader in his field,
found the structure he called the "endorestiform nucleus" through
close study of thousands of thin slices of brain tissue. To date, after
studying a number of mammals, including primates, Paxinos and his
team have found this nucleus to be unique to humans. Moreover, the
nucleus has neural connections with many other parts of the brain,
indicating that it is most likely a coordination center for fine motor
function, an attribute exclusive to *Homo sapiens*.

While Paxinos remains a supporter of evolutionary theory, his
discovery gives rise to some interesting questions. One of these is
based on the fact that a brain nucleus contains the cell bodies of
many neurons. Its presence means that something cellular has been
added to the basic primate "cerebral blueprint," if we can use that
term. But like the fossil record, there seems to be no "intermediate
forms" of this structure—it just appears in the human brain and in
no other. Perhaps in no better anatomical way does it differentiate us
from the apes. So the obvious question is, How did it get there?

There are many other functional differences between the brains
of humans and other mammals. These include higher cognitive

functions such as consciousness, speech, artistic and musical appreciation, empathy, logical thinking including inference, hypothesis formation, memory, and ideation, to mention a few. The learning process in humans is therefore far more complicated than the behavior patterns of other species. Another unique feature is that human learning is transmissible to others, chiefly owing to speech, the fine motor functions of writing, and our color stereoscopic vision that permits the latter. Some of these attributes appear to have no evolutionary survival advantage. In my experience, this bears witness to a privileged position of *Homo sapiens* granted by a higher Power.[7]

The unique, functional anatomy of *Homo sapiens* differentiates us so widely from other, even superficially-similar mammals, that it is perhaps best expressed by this statement: "Then God said, 'Let us make mankind in our image'" (Gen. 1:26).

33

A Mind for Beauty

L. James Gibson

Beauty is something we all enjoy. Behind my home is a ridge of hills that I frequently climb in the morning to see the beauty of the sunrise. If I walk in a different direction in the evening, I can enjoy the colors of the sunset. As I take my hikes, I occasionally see wild animals—coyotes, rabbits, donkeys, birds of various kinds. Although I have visited the sites many times and enjoyed the beauty of the skies, I have never seen any of the wild animals pay any attention to the beauty that has attracted my attention. What is it that makes me see beauty, and why is my response so different from that of the animals around me?

Color is one aspect that contributes to our appreciation of beauty. The colors of sunrise and sunset attract our attention to the skies at those particular moments in time. Another example is the rainbow, with its spectrum of color that elicits our attention and admiration. Other examples include our choices of clothing, home décor, automobiles, works of art, and many natural objects such as birds and butterflies. The ability to see and distinguish colors requires a complex visual system, working in conjunction with the occipital lobe of the brain.[1] Most vertebrates and many invertebrates are able to distinguish colors, and some have enlarged optical lobes that enable impressive visual abilities. Many species rely on color patterns to identify conspecifics. Yet with the exception of humans, none of these species is known to appreciate color patterns for their beauty.

Form is another aspect of beauty. For example, we tend to appreciate the form of objects that have symmetry. Bilateral symmetry is a part of beauty that is so familiar we may not think about it until we encounter an example that has been damaged. We may admire a horse as it gallops freely across a meadow, but if that same horse has a deformed leg or other damage to its symmetry, we immediately notice the defect.

Other forms of symmetry include radial symmetry and spiral symmetry. These forms also attract our admiration. Radial symmetry occurs when a form has a central axis around which the parts are arranged so that it can be divided into two equal halves in more than one plane. Many flowers have radial symmetry, including roses, daisies, and lilies. Many cnidarians are radially symmetrical, and echinoderms typically have five-fold radial symmetry.

Spiral symmetry occurs when the parts are arranged regularly in a rotational pattern around a central axis. If the spiral coils on a plane, the result is planar spiral symmetry, such as is seen in the shell of the chambered nautilus or the fiddleneck pattern of a young fern. If the spiral coils around the central axis, the result is vertical spiral symmetry such as in top shells, augers, and many other gastropod shells. Spiral symmetry is also seen in pine cones and, in a related pattern, the famous helix of DNA. Such symmetry attracts our attention and contributes to our perception of beauty.

Identification of form is a type of pattern recognition that is vital to most metazoan animals. It functions in finding food, identifying potential predators or mates, orientation of motility, identification of location, etc. Thus, all visually oriented multicellular organisms must have brains that facilitate pattern recognition. In mammals, this is accomplished in the cortex.[2] Birds do not have a brain cortex but recognize patterns in an area of the brain known as the dorsal ventricular ridge. Despite the fact that pattern recognition is a vital and widespread ability among many types of animals, there is no evidence that animals enjoy beauty for its own sake.

A third aspect of beauty is proportion. For many people, there is beauty in mathematically regular shapes and proportions.[3] The so-called golden ratio is a well-known example of the beauty of proportion. The golden ratio is related to the Fibonacci Series, a mathematical sequence in which each number is equal to the sum of the preceding two numbers, beginning with 0 and 1. Dividing a Fibonacci number by its preceding number gives a ratio that approaches 1.618 as the numbers get larger. It is widely recognized that a rectangle in which the proportion of the width to the height is about 1.618 is visually pleasing, which is why it is called the golden rectangle. Many examples have been reported in art, architecture, and nature, although there is some controversy over some of the claims that have been made.

The appreciation of visual beauty is a pleasurable experience that involves a complex series of connections in the human brain. These connections include the default network, which studies have linked to the sensation of pleasure when viewing objects.[4] The prefrontal cortex is a core part of the default network and is present in most, if not all, mammals. Similar structures appear to be present in birds. Apes have a prefrontal cortex that appears very similar to ours,[5] except that the human cortex seems to have space for many more connections. It seems that many animals have brains that are generally similar to the human brain but without the neural connections needed for appreciation of beauty.

Beauty is a sense of admiration and pleasure that requires a complex brain with particular connections that seem to be possessed only by humans. Why should humans be so unique in this? The best answer I have seen is that humans were created in the image of a Creator who loves beauty, and that our brains were designed to be able to share the appreciation of beauty with our Creator.

PART VII

Interdependence and Cooperation

34

Designed for Maternal Bonding

Rowena R. Antemano

Bonding or attachment is a basic instinct that binds the helpless newborn and the mother, real or surrogate. This mysterious but automatic binding relationship is symbiotic—favoring survival for the infant and affiliation of intimacy for the mother. Newborn babies sleeping alone on cot beds next to their mothers even for a short time have significantly higher heart rate and more restless sleep than those who co-sleep with their mothers and have skin-to-skin contact.[1] A fascinating animal study by Harry Harlow shows that baby monkeys prefer to cling onto a terry cloth mother than a wire mother with a milk bottle attached to it.[2] Mother's intimacy is the environment most comfortable and restful during the early years of life.

Forming an unconscious but deep and permanent emotional bond at infancy is called "filial imprinting," a term coined by a Nobel laureate, Konrad Lorenz, a behavioral ornithologist. Filial imprinting solidifies within a narrow window of time during infancy when the brain is most susceptible and sensitive to environmental stimuli.[3] In humans, the first three years of life determine the lifetime closeness and belongingness between the child and caregiver, primarily the mother. In animals, ewes lick their own lambs within four hours of giving birth in order to recognize their offspring from other young born to the flocks of sheep that graze that same time of year. Infant rats develop a lifetime preference to the smell similar to the nipples of the dam they suck during the first week of life, but not later.

Separation from the mother, the main caregiver, early in life spoils the filial imprinting.[4] It disturbs the immature and sensitive molecular, cellular, neurological, and physiological development of the individual with a long-term impact. Experts believe that psychiatric disorders, depression, anxiety, and addiction in adults originate from a compromising environment of infancy. Poor performance on memory, behavioral response, decision-making, fear or anxiety, and coping strategies later in life is a projection of the emotional damage sustained in the early years of life.

Emotional stress early in life has an undeniable impact on the cellular and molecular components of the brain[5] in adult experimental animals, particularly rats. For example, it reduces both the number of branches and connections of neurons in the medial frontal cortex, the region for emotional control and social behavior. It reduces production of neurotransmitters while increasing the production of neuroinflammatory molecules in the limbic regions, which are associated with mood disorders. It reduces long-term potential signals in the hippocampus, amygdala, and prefrontal cortex, loosening the bond between synapses and resulting in reduced memory and inadequate emotionality. It also delays the production of neurotransmitters for the optimal development and function of the brain.

Initially, I was neither a believer nor a fan of the so-called early separation research. When my professor assigned me to investigate its impact on young astrocytes, I rebelliously but silently agreed. My study was to answer the question, What is the impact of the early separation on astrocytes in the prefrontal cortex of infant trumpet-tailed rats, *Octodon degus*? My experimental strategy mimicked the separation in human babies from their mother during the pre-weaning stage.

I investigated the astrocytes in the prefrontal cortex of the brains of infant rats. As I watched infant rats scream in panic inside the isolation boxes searching for the dam, it seemed it was all behavioral, an outward reaction without any neurobiological component. But seeing through the microscope the damaged, broken, shrunken, and disfigured growing astrocytes, their reduced cell count, reduced branching complexity as well as reduced protein expression all due to separation,[6] I changed my mind. I realized that bonding is innate in all living things, particularly mammals. It is ingrained in the microscopic cells of the brain; separation is debilitating. Depending on the time and degree of exposure, separation may delay, disable, and/or stagnate the brain development for emotional and social control.

Astrocytes are indispensable partners for neurons in the mammalian brain.[7] They participate extensively in the formation, maturation, maintenance, and function of the brain for the entire period of development. During early development, astrocytes release gliotrophic and neurotrophic factors for neurite growth and extension in sculpting, pruning, and guiding the neurons to their final destinations in the brain. In the mature brain, astrocytes are active partners of neurons in synapses. They release gliotransmitters like glutamate that act on themselves and on neurons in order to propagate and regulate synaptic transmission. They are positioned strategically so that a single astrocyte may contact as many synapses as possible. They also form blood-brain barriers to prevent blood from entering the brain. During brain injury, they patch the affected site, forming a glial scar.

In recent decades, the hyperproliferation of astrocytes has become a prominent biomarker in neurological and psychiatric pathologies including Alzheimer's Disease, Parkinson's Disease, Down syndrome, depression, and schizophrenia.[8] Yes, astrocytes are emotional. They respond to emotional stress, which I was privileged to observe firsthand.

In summary, bonding is a universal instinct initiated by God for the benefit of humans. We are made to attach, relate, and be emotional, intimate social beings—a reflection of who God is. The God of love plans that He bonds with us from eternity to eternity.

35

A Tale of Two Enzymes

George T. Javor

Shortly after beginning my studies for a PhD in biochemistry at Columbia University, I came face to face with an unexpected, very difficult situation. In a laboratory session I was asked to kill a cute white laboratory rat, remove its liver, and study the synthesis of cholesterol. During my undergraduate work for a BS degree in chemistry I did not take any course in biology where animals were routinely dissected. I was devastated as I performed the gruesome task, and I could not see myself repeatedly killing animals in the future. Fortunately, there were laboratories in the biochemistry department that worked with microorganisms rather than animals. I joined one such laboratory and did my research for the degree on the bacterium *Escherichia coli* (*E. coli*).

I spent my subsequent 39 years in "*E.-coli* land," happily digging into the mysteries of this fascinating organism.[1] Along the way I encountered numerous examples of the Creator's unspeakable genius, such as the mystery of two enzymes: β-galactosidase in *Escherichia coli* and alcohol dehydrogenase in the human liver.

Undergirding all life processes are thousands of chemical changes. Enzymes, mostly proteins, are formidable and complex molecular machines, which promote and control every chemical change.

For my PhD thesis work, I studied how a unique variety of *E. coli* synthesized the enzyme β-galactosidase. *E. coli* cells manufacture more than 4,000 different types of proteins, but not all at the same time. Bacterial cells only make the proteins that are needed for growth at that time. The bacterium produces this enzyme when it encounters the milk sugar, lactose. Beta-galactosidase facilitates the rapid cleavage of this double sugar to glucose and galactose, and the bacterium gobbles up glucose for growth.

At the time of my studies, no one understood why *E. coli* cells produced β-galactosidase because, while the bacterium resides in the human colon, lactose never makes it that far during digestion.

More recently it was discovered that the double-sugar lactose is not the only substance that can evoke the synthesis of β-galactosidase in *E. coli.* A compound called β-galactosyl glycerol will do it just as well. And where do we find β-galactosyl glycerol, but in the indigestible content of vegetable matter of our diet, which actually travels all the way to the colon.

We learn from the Bible that the Creator designated fruits, nuts, and seed-bearing plants as food for humans. Thus He made provision for the lowly *E. coli* to live on the crumbs of our vegetarian diet.

But why was it so important for humans to have happy *E. coli* cells in their colons? Because most of the hundreds of species of microorganisms residing in our colons are "obligate anaerobes," that is, they can live only in oxygen-free environments. Air is toxic for these microbes. The main task of *E. coli* cells in the colon is to preserve an oxygen-free environment. *E. coli* cells are excellent oxygen scavengers. Along with other colon bacteria, *E. coli* also makes vitamin K and biotin and protects the gut from pathogenic organisms.

Five genes on human chromosome #4, ADH1-ADH5, direct the manufacture of five versions of the liver enzyme, alcohol dehydrogenase. These enzymes convert ethyl alcohol to acetaldehyde, which then is utilized for energy. However, their presence in the liver is a conundrum because the human body does not produce ethyl alcohol. A professor in graduate school explained this curiosity to us students, but did not offer a solution. Many years later, while teaching bacterial physiology to graduate students, the solution finally occurred to me.

In the oxygen-free environment of the colon, *E. coli* exhibits a "mixed acid fermentation" type of metabolism where one of the secreted substances is ethyl alcohol. Alcohol finds its way into the bloodstream when it is absorbed in the colon along with water. Were it not for the mysterious alcohol dehydrogenase in our liver, all of us would walk around inebriated!

So the mystery of both enzymes is solved. The Creator, who placed *E. coli* and other microorganisms in the human colon for our benefit, inserted the requisite gene for this enzyme into human chromosome #4, keeping Adam and Eve and their offspring from being continually intoxicated!

The creationist's understanding of the biosphere—that the welfare of each organism hinges on support from other living entities—is clearly illustrated here. This concept may serve us well when we are searching for solutions to other apparent conundrums in nature.

36

The Marvel of a Functioning Ecosystem

Warren A. Shipton

The special garden in Eden was part of a broader whole, as illustrated when Adam and Eve were expelled from it. From the beginning humans played an essential role in maintaining the integrity of the ecosystem in which they were placed, for they were to "tend and keep it" (Gen. 2:15, NKJV). The Creation account indicates that there were aquatic and terrestrial ecosystems and that abundant life-forms were present (Gen. 1:20–25; Ps. 104:14–18, 25–27). Diversity and the richness of interactions among organisms are essential for ecosystem stability.

The interacting design features built into such systems is portrayed when photosynthesizing plants were assigned for human and animal use (Gen. 1:29, 30), and when one considers that, the design of animals dictates that the unused portions of the organic matter consumed is voided. The organic material breakdown process involves enzymes released by the consuming organism and by the multitudinous gut microbes. The deconstructing process by microbes continues in the soil (part of the invisible creation, Col. 1:16).

Terrestrial plants were created to perform roles such as recycling gases and providing food resources for a variety of living organisms. Parallel roles are performed by photosynthetic organisms in aquatic habitats, for God provided food for the life-forms there (Ps. 104:25–27).

It is significant that in performing the assigned roles in terrestrial and aquatic environments, portions (or all) of the photosynthetic organism cease to exist. Hence, we sow seeds to get new plants (the seeds perish), we observe granivory and frugivory (energy transfer occurs), and zooplankton eat phytoplankton. The indicated loss of life does not involve the shedding of blood or cessation of breathing. Such events, familiar today (e.g., carnivory, slaughter), come as a consequence of the Fall (Lev. 17:13, 14; Eccl. 3:19; cf. Isa. 11:6–9).

The cessation of life noted in organisms capable of using inorganic nutrients and photosynthesis (or chemosynthesis) as a source of energy represents a servant-design role that has clear parallels with ideal Christian behavior and future experience (John 12:24; 13:12–17; 1 Cor. 15:35–38).

Dysfunction and degeneration in nature came as a result of human disobedience (Gen. 2:17; 3:16–19). All Creation was affected (Rom. 8:22). Through these changes, the intended purpose and usefulness of life-forms was frustrated, and functional goals became difficult or impossible to achieve, partly due to the time constraints imposed by the premature cessation of biochemical operations (biological death). Human moral failure has additional consequences: unrepentant humans will be subjected to the second (eternal) death (Rev. 20:6–10).

The unicellular aquatic photosynthesizers (e.g., coccolithophores, diatoms, dinoflagellates, cryptophytes) perform their primary production function well.[1] Then the next design function of many follows, serving as a food source for a myriad of other life-forms among the zooplankton. In formal scientific language, this serving involves an engulfing (phagocytosis, a form of endocytosis) or a grazing process. Having served, their remains are recycled by bacteria. Some dinoflagellates are found living in corals and marine invertebrates to provide energy in their role as beneficiaries. In return, they receive selected nutrients.

Similar beneficiary roles involving microbes are commonly found in terrestrial environments among plants and animals. The latter is illustrated by ruminant animals, which possess a special fermentation chamber (rumen) inhabited by a range of microbes (bacteria, fungi, protozoa, and others). They deconstruct the living plant tissues to provide energy for the animal. In complex processes, a majority of the protein required for animal sustenance is often provided by bacteria. In return, the microbes are given a special environment to enable their continued existence.[2] Survival elsewhere is not assured. Microbes provide many benefits to other animals in that they assist in the balanced development of the body and the operation of the immune system,[3] both essential for the "very good" designation given in the beginning (Gen. 1:31). The concept of giving and receiving is a fundamental aspect of God's plans for our planet (e.g., marriage). We receive from our great Benefactor in order to give (Matt. 10:8; Acts 10:35).

The deconstructing role of microbes is one of their most representative activities. It is, in reality, a service role in that useful materials are provided for other organisms to ensure their continued functioning. It also represents a humble role (cf. Christian experience, 1 Pet. 5:5).

In studying the interactions defining current ecosystems, a range of promoting and dampening activities are involved. The scriptural record makes it clear that the infliction of anxiety, pain, and death were not in God's original plan (Rev. 21:4; cf. Isa. 65:25). Seed (Hebrew: *zera*) and seed-bearing plants are mentioned six times in Genesis 1, emphasizing their significance. The study of these plants and their aquatic equivalents, ranging from seed germination, pollination,[4] fertilization, and other events, shows that promoting and controlling activities are hardwired into the operation of a stable ecosystem. Significantly, clear parallels can be drawn with the excitatory and inhibitory actions noted when nerves pass signals via neurotransmitter molecules to other cells in mammals. The process involves both exocytosis and endocytosis.[5] This would appear to establish interactions of a stimulatory and inhibitory nature as part of the design complexity seen at the system level at the beginning. In ecosystems, the complexity of interactions is vital for the maintenance of stability. A complete understanding of the original ecosystem dynamics is, however, beyond current knowledge.

37

Cooperation, Empathy, and Altruism in Nature

Noemí Durán

Why are we here? Where did we come from? Possible answers to these questions vary widely but can be summarized into two main categories: design and chance. Either we were meant to be and there is a reason and a purpose to our existence, or we are just the fortunate product of a series of extraordinarily unlikely accidents governed solely by natural laws.

The Bible affirms that we were carefully designed by a wise, all-powerful God who created out of love and provided good resources for the sake and happiness of His creatures. At the end of the creative task, God determined that everything He had made was "very good" (Gen. 1:31).

Conversely, materialistic accounts of origins portray us and all other earthlings as the unforeseen outcome of biological evolution. This natural process of change over time is said to be driven by natural selection, a mechanism commonly associated with struggle, violence, and death. The weak die, the strong live; organisms fight ruthlessly with their peers for control over limited resources; the fittest succeed and reproduce at the expense of the less fit.

This is the type of environment featured in classical wildlife documentaries: life is harsh in the African savanna, where a sickly zebra ends up being devoured by vultures and hyenas, crocodiles feast on the slowest wildebeests crossing the river, and a male lion savagely kills cubs that are not his. If natural selection is both the facilitator and the governor of life on Earth, the discouraging answer to the question of our origin is that there is no transcendent reason for our existence. The only purpose driving living beings is to survive for another day.

Nature, however, happens to be much more complex than scientists and documentary producers believe it to be. Many studies have shown a different view of how organisms interact with each other. Hundreds of articles have been published on what are called "prosocial" behaviors especially seen among animals that live in social groups, such as dolphins, elephants, and chimpanzees. Members of a pod, herd, or troop do not spend their days constantly fighting each other. On the contrary, it is common to find them cooperating in group tasks, such as food acquisition, or assisting a comrade in trouble. Dolphins team up to keep injured companions at the water's surface,[1] and elephants rescue individuals that have fallen into holes.[2]

Dozens of articles and hundreds of observations on chimpanzees document their propensity to appease upset partners, console those who are distressed, and help peers in need. An emblematic case was reported in the Yerkes National Primate Research Center at Emory University, which houses a large colony of chimpanzees. Peony, an old female, had arthritis and could not walk or climb normally. Several younger females helped her climb by pushing her from the back and brought her water from a fountain by carrying it in their mouths.[3] In a wild population in Tanzania, a female chimpanzee was observed caring for a severely disabled baby that could not walk, sit, or climb on its own because of spinal damage. With the aid of an older daughter, she managed to keep the baby alive for almost two years.[4]

As many scientists have realized, these types of behaviors reveal a profound emotional awareness in animals. Several biologists who have been studying very different species have reached this conclusion. Frans de Waal, who works mainly with primates, has written several books on the extraordinary emotional capacities of these animals. Peggy Mason, who works with rats, designed with her team a series of experiments to assess whether rats feel empathy, and the results were unequivocal.[5] She believes that "acting on empathic feelings to help another in need is a biological and in fact a neurobiological mandate. It's in our brain."[6]

Finding that diverse animals, from rats to elephants, have a deep concern for others sheds light on our original questions. A world where animals and people are preprogrammed to connect and care aligns well with the biblical account of a God of love who created humans in His image.

Secular scientists who intend to explain empathy from an evolutionary perspective[7] argue that animal groups with strong bonds among their members might be more successful at leaving descendants. Empathy, which promotes bonding, could have been favored by natural selection after its random appearance in some ancestor far back in the evolution of animals.

Although plausible, this hypothesis falls short of explaining how natural selection could maintain specific altruistic behaviors such as the care of the elderly or the disabled, which do not increase reproductive rates yet increase costs in time and energy. Even more difficult to explain are altruistic behaviors like the adoption of a baby of a different species, which has been documented at least twice in the wild.[8]

To me, there is a much more parsimonious and harmonious explanation for cooperation, empathy, and altruism than slow acquisition during evolution. The God of the Bible, whose very essence is love, empathy, and selflessness, so deeply embedded these features in the brains of the creatures He designed that thousands of years of sin have not been able to erase them completely.

PART VIII

Out of Eden

38 ●

Epigenetic Inheritance: A Mechanism of Adaptation

Wellington dos Santos Silva

Epigenetics generally refers to phenotypes and processes that are transmitted to other cells and sometimes to future generations, but are not the result of differences in the sequence of DNA bases. Epigenetic effects are caused by changes in gene expression resulting from changes in chromatin or other aspects of the structure of genetic material. Often, these changes occur in response to the environment, food, and even to social interactions.[1]

A fundamental precept of evolutionary biology is that natural selection acts on phenotypes determined by the variation of the DNA sequence in natural populations. However, advances in understanding gene regulation have elucidated a spectrum of epigenetic molecular phenomena capable of profoundly altering temporal and spatial patterns of gene expression without changing the sequence of bases in the DNA.

The best understood mechanism of epigenetic change is DNA methylation, which refers to the addition of methyl groups to the nucleotide bases. In eukaryotes, the predominant type of DNA methylation is the methylation of cytosine to produce 5-methylcytosine. This is associated with inhibition of transcription and often occurs in the cytosine bases that are immediately adjacent to guanine nucleotides, called CpG dinucleotides. In the CpG dinucleotides, the cytosine nucleotides in the two DNA strands are diagonal in relation to each other (see Figure 38-1).

Throughout my academic training I have always been taught

that random mutations are the source of genetic variability upon which natural selection operates. With rare exceptions, the literature shows this mechanism acting slowly. However, in the last two decades, many papers have challenged this paradigm by showing that epigenetic mechanisms are involved in very rapid phenotypic changes that are inherited by the offspring. In the evolutionist world-view, the terminology "selected for" or "selected against" is used to describe the survival or demise of an organism. This use mistakenly seems to ascribe primary causality to the environment as if it were imposing its will through a mystical or undetectable event of selection.[2] However, there is a difference between the naturalist worldview and the design-based worldview that shifts primary causality to the preparation of genetic and epigenetic systems designed to respond to environmental changes. These systems were designed to produce self-tuning organisms and fill environments with the creation of new ecological niches in virtually every place on Earth.

Representative examples highlight innate genetic systems in all the diverse taxonomic groups demonstrating successful characteristics in determining whether an organism survives in a new environment. These systems consist of elaborate networks of genes that have the information to help organisms address environmental challenges in real time. One component of these innate genetic systems is molecules called "chaperones," which help to fold proteins in the right way. The concentration of these molecules can be proportional to the stressful exposures found by multicellular organisms, and their concentration directly affects the expression of significant characteristics in such a way that their modulation can either reveal or hide the phenotypic

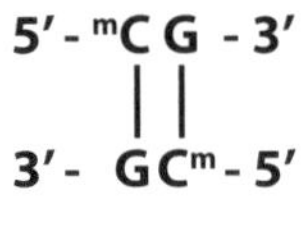

$$5' - {}^{m}C \ G - 3'$$
$$| \ |$$
$$3' - \ GC^{m} - 5'$$

FIGURE 38-1. In eukaryotes, cytosine is the most frequently methylated nitrogenous base, yielding a 5-methylcytosine.

effects of natural variation. Chaperones have been implicated as a major factor in significant morphological changes such as the loss of eyes in a kind of cave fish, *Astyanax mexicanus*.[3] On the basis of fundamental interactions of the sensor system, these fish can feel water conductivity ranging up to five times more in caves compared to surface currents. Embryos from fish that grow under conditions of low conductivity positively regulate the genes of chaperone molecules.

Darwin's finches, which inhabit the Galápagos Archipelago, constitute an iconic model for studies of speciation and adaptive evolution. In an attempt to verify species changes in real time, two renowned researchers conducted a study for 30 uninterrupted years between 1972 and 2001 on one of the Galápagos Islands to study Darwin's finches.

Between 1976 and 1977, they verified that body and beak size of the finch *Geospiza fortis* decreased between 1984 and 1986; beak shape for this same species became thinner and remained so for the next 15 years. A different finch, *Geospiza scandens*, showed a gradual and uniform decrease in beak size and a rectilinear trend in beak shape, converging with the morphological characteristics of the *Geospiza fortis* beak. The researchers found that periods in which finches showed more marked changes in morphology and beak size were the same in which there was rain scarcity and changes in composition of the supply of seeds.[4]

The neo-Darwinian model of evolution requires random mutations to generate the phenotypic variation necessary for natural selection to act. However, what process provoked the morphological alterations of the finches' beaks observed in short periods of environmental stress? Epigenetic inheritance has been shown to be a good model to explain gene expression patterns that have generated phenotypic differences in finches and their offspring,[5] but such hereditary changes are not associated with mutations, recombination, or anything associated with the nucleotide sequence. Rather, they are simply associated with the activation and/or inactivation of genes.

The examples presented above illustrate the innate capacity for self-tuning as a basic characteristic of all living things. These remarkable observations show us the design of organisms created to fill the earth with its dynamic and challenging environments. Therefore, the field of epigenetics offers great opportunity for creationists to develop research that demonstrates evidence for design and helps to strengthen faith in the Creator.

39

Designed Genetically to Survive Catastrophe

Delano S. Lewis

The specialized fields of taxonomy and systematics currently hold the theory of evolution as an essential dogma. This is in marked contrast to the thinking of many early naturalists who did not hold a naturalistic view of the origin of life. The founder of modern taxonomy, Carolus Linnaeus (Carl Linnaeus or Carl von Linné) wrote in the preface to one of his latter works: "The Earth's creation is the glory of God, as seen from the works of Nature by Man alone."[1] In his view, the study of nature would reveal the order of God's creation. It would be good to be free to explore scientific enquiry with similar sentiments, and it is with these sentiments and the postulate that nature is designed to survive environmental disturbance by adapting to stress that this chapter is written. This order in nature can be seen in three specific processes: genetic recombination, epigenetic effects, and gene mutations.

Through the processes of genetic recombination (crossing over), epigenetic effects (DNA methylation and histone modification), and gene mutations, species can possess significant diversity. This diversity is necessary for the genetic health of any population, often mitigating the effects of genetic bottlenecking and reducing the threat of species extinctions, which are preceded by a loss of genetic diversity within species caused by sharp reduction in population sizes due to environmental stress.[2] Individuals of the same species may exhibit differences in the expression of the same genes (phenotypic plasticity). Both genetic diversity and phenotypic plasticity[3] are drivers in the process of speciation leading to the species biodiversity we see today.

In most sexually reproducing organisms, offspring are never genetically the same except for monozygotic multiples. This variation in the genes inherited is produced by the meiotic cell cycle. Unlike the mitotic cell cycle, which occurs in somatic cells and produces two cells identical to the original parent cell, meiosis only occurs in reproductive cells and produces four cells that contain a different genetic composition from each other and possess only half of the genetic material of the original cell. This diversity in genetic composition arises during a phase of meiosis in which chromosomes can temporarily overlap and fuse their arms, causing a crossover or recombination of genetic material. It is here that diversity in sexual reproducing organisms is initiated. Several other factors also influence genetic diversity; however, these factors are secondary. Recombination should be viewed as the initiation of genetic diversity among individual offspring of sexually reproducing organisms.

DNA methylation occurs when methyl groups are added to the DNA molecule. This changes the activity of that segment of DNA without changing the DNA sequence itself. Histone modifications affect the structure of the proteins (histones) that package DNA, and this affects gene expression. Environmental stimuli, or stress, promote epigenetic changes that, in turn, generate differences in the expression of DNA sequences;[4] this leads to changes in the heritable characters across generations. These changes are often expressed as increased stress tolerance and destabilized genomes (genetic diversity). Epigenetic regulations are the source of these changes, and their effects can be seen as early as in the immediate offspring and may persist beyond the ensuing generation,[5] but are not permanent and often persist as long as the population is exposed to the causative environmental stress. This plasticity in the expression of a genetic code (phenotypic plasticity) is essential for the adaptability and survival of populations.

Genetic mutations are permanent modifications to the DNA sequence of an organism and are often viewed as errors as they most often adversely affect an organism's survival. Mutations that are not the cause of diseases or other deleterious effects may be neutral (of no effect) or offer increased survivability to the individual, population, or species in which it occurs. While it is generally accepted that the majority of mutations are either neutral or deleterious, the ones that are beneficial are often of significant importance to the survival of organisms, population, and species. Mutations, therefore, can be viewed as a genetic lottery system in which the survivability of the species, not the individual, is increased over time as its random mutations are exposed to non-random selection processes. This is a deliberate design to allow species to increase genetic diversity over time.

In whatever cells gene mutations occur and whatever the results of genetic recombination are, the expression of these genes is environmentally modulated through epigenetic influences. We can view genetic recombination as designed to affect the survivability of the individual. Epigenetic effects on genes that result in differences in the expressions of those genes (phenotypic plasticity) may be viewed as having been designed to affect the ensuing generations or populations exposed to a catastrophe. Random gene mutations and the non-random selection processes that act on them may be designed to affect the survivability of a species over time for the long term. These processes are specifically designed to enable, respectively, individuals, populations, and species to survive in an ever-changing environment and to adapt to catastrophic events, be they a global flood, volcanic eruption, drought, severe heat, extreme cold, or another environmental stress.

40

Adapting to Life after a Catastrophe

Tiago A. J. de Souza

Regardless of the worldview adopted, much evidence in the fields of geology and paleontology points to the occurrence of catastrophic events during the history of our planet. Based on the disasters that occur today, we can conjecture that past global catastrophic events caused climatic changes and affected the availability of food. Therefore, in a post-catastrophic context, surviving organisms were challenged to adapt to hostile living conditions.

In addition to the survival of the fittest advocated by natural selection, organisms in these post-catastrophic situations are also able to respond adaptively. This adaptation involves genetic and epigenetic changes. To understand how this might have occurred, we will consider the worm *Caenorhabditis elegans* (*C. elegans*). This nematode has been widely used as a model in different research fields, resulting in some scientific studies awarded with Nobel Prizes. In genetic studies, it is possible to correlate findings in *C. elegans* with several other organisms including humans, since 40% of its sequences are homologous to those found in humans.

Studies analyzing the response of *C. elegans* to different types of stress have demonstrated that this nematode not only presents beneficial epigenetic modifications during stress situations but is also capable of passing these changes to subsequent generations, allowing them to better deal with stresses of a similar nature.[1] Among other effects, epigenetic alterations can modify the genomic structure through the contraction or expansion of repetitive DNA. In addition, the modulation of these repetitive regions may increase the rate of evolution, resulting in drastic phenotypic changes over a few generations. Therefore, during stressful conditions related to post-catastrophic environments, surviving organisms could present genomic and phenotypic changes over a short time.[2] However, this is only one of the mechanisms capable of generating genomic and morphological changes much faster than those for which Darwinian gradualism advocates. Another mechanism that will be addressed in this chapter is the dynamic of transposing genetic elements in response to stress situations.

Also known as "transposons," these elements have the ability to move from one genomic site to the other through the action of transposase enzymes that act by breaking the phosphodiester bonds present between the nucleotides and DNA double strands. The activities of the transposons can result in deletions, inversions, and chromosomal fusions having the potential to cause some diseases as well as to generate new genetic information. About 12% of the genome of *C. elegans* is formed by transposons, and the vast majority of these elements have lost their transposition capacity.

The ability to adjust to external disturbances is an essential property for all living organisms. In this context, the dynamic nature of the transposition elements active in *C. elegans* is essential for the organization of the genome in response to different stress situations. Temperature variations and oxidation are some examples of stressful conditions capable of inducing the expression of transposon genes.[3] Recent analyses have shown that even moderate exposure to these stresses is already capable of increasing the excision of transposons in a concentration-dependent manner.[4] The transposons respond to different stresses through transcriptional activator sites located in these elements that act as a system of defense against genomic disorganization. Some of these sites, for example, are very similar to those found in heat shock proteins. Interestingly, some heat shock proteins can act by regulating the action of the transposing elements in *C. elegans* during stress.[5]

In order for the response of stress-transposable elements to be adequate, there are mechanisms that regulate transposition at the transcriptional and post-transcriptional levels by means of epigenetic modifications and silencing by RNA interference (RNAi), respectively. At the transcriptional level, DNA compaction dramatically compromises, or decreases, the expression of transposable elements. Therefore, depending on the transcriptional modifications, especially of the N-terminal amino tails of the histones, the expression of transposable elements can be induced or repressed. In addition to this, it should be considered that under stress conditions DNA tends to decompress. Therefore, it is clearly noticeable that these two mechanisms of adaptation to stress situations are closely related.

The genomic dynamics in response to stresses in various organisms, including *C. elegans,* depend on the harmony between external stimuli and mechanisms of internal gene regulation and allow the genome of that organism to adapt to stress situations. Thus, stressful conditions related to post-catastrophic scenarios could cause epigenetic modifications and mobilization of transposition elements, and these events are interconnected. In addition, inhospitable post-catastrophic scenarios provide the opportunity for surviving populations to quickly occupy different niches and adapt to them.

The fine-tuning between these mechanisms of stress response and the emergence of adaptive changes is a strong evidence that the genomes of organisms (e.g., *C. elegans*) were designed to adapt to adverse conditions ensuing a catastrophe. Moreover, the unpredictable nature of disasters makes it very difficult to defend the Darwinian concept that mechanisms of genomic adaptation to such catastrophic scenarios could evolve gradually. Considering the information presented in this chapter, we can conjecture that epigenetic mechanisms and genetic transposition could have facilitated micro-evolutionary processes allowing the origin, over a few generations, of a large biodiversity from ancestral populations that had occupied the empty niches left after global catastrophes, such as the one described in chapters 6 to 8 of the book of Genesis.

41

Mass Extinctions in the Fossil Record

Roberto E. Biaggi

A recent scientific paper that received great news coverage described the immediate effects of the Chicxulub meteoritic impact and its role in the Cretaceous-Paleogene extinction.[1] At the Tanis site in southwestern North Dakota, ejecta, sediments, and a mass death mixture of marine and continental organisms were "emplaced immediately (minutes to hours) after the impact" and it is suggested "that the depositional event, calculated to have coincided with the arrival of seismic waves from Chicxulub, likely resulted from a seismically coupled local seiche.... The global extinction event, therefore could have had a rapidly delivered precursor, both at the local and global scales, minutes after impact."[2]

This explicit link between catastrophe and extinction captures the intent of this essay, which describes two major characteristics of the fossil record recognized today by mainstream science: (1) the worldwide occurrence of five main "mass extinctions" and of many more "smaller extinctions" that affected a lower number of taxa, but are still detectable and significant; and (2) the occurrence of numerous mass mortality events (aside from major extinctions) in the ocean and also on land, in which hundreds to thousands of organisms died quite simultaneously and are now often preserved as exceptional deposits.

The fossil record of the Phanerozoic (Cambrian to Recent) preserves numerous global and abrupt changes, interpreted as mass extinctions, in which many different animal and plant taxa disappear. Today, most authors recognize five major mass extinction horizons:

Upper Ordovician, Upper Devonian, Permian-Triassic (P-T) boundary, Triassic-Jurassic (T-J) boundary, and Cretaceous-Paleogene
(K-Pg) boundary. It has been calculated that at each of these major
horizons at least 70% of the marine species present in underlying
strata became extinct. Surprisingly, however, over 90% of past species
disappear at intervals other than the Big Five mass extinctions.[3] Many
maintain that the greatest of mass extinctions is documented at the
P-T boundary. However, the K-Pg boundary extinction is probably
the most famous, because it includes the dinosaurs and its suspected
cause of a massive bolide impact (the much-studied Chicxulub
impact event).[4]

Some authors agree that there is evidence for at least 20–28 other
minor extinction events in the Phanerozoic record.[5] One recent study
reviewed approximately 20 biotic crises between the Cambrian and
the end Cretaceous and suggests that for many of these events and
proximal killers, volcanism is a major driver of mass extinction.[6] In
addition, there are many more, perhaps myriads of localized mass
mortality events, areas in which hundreds of specimens have died
and are preserved, sometimes in an exceptional way (i.e., completely
articulated or with soft tissues). Examples include the exquisite 3D
preserved fossil fish of the Cretaceous Romualdo Formation from
NE Brazil, tens of thousands of specimens of the dinosaur *Maiasau-
rus* as well as eggs with embryos from Montana, and the famous
Cleveland-Lloyd Quarry in Utah that contains approximately 12,000
bones of 12 species of dinosaurs.

There has been much debate on the actual causes of extinctions. The many possibilities offered include flood basalts (massive
and widespread lava flows, such as the Deccan Traps of India and
the Siberian Traps); asteroid collisions (such as the Chicxulub
impact event); major drops in sea level; global warming; global
cooling; methane eruptions; anoxic events with drops in oxygen
availability in the oceans; and other effects stemming from plate
reconfigurations, ocean acidification, and poisoning by toxic trace
metals.[7] It has proven difficult to pinpoint proximate and direct

causes for any extinction, and it is more likely that the ultimate cause might be a combination of multiple mechanisms with varying effects on different environments.

Notwithstanding this debate on triggering mechanisms, it has become evident that the geologic column contains a record of hundreds of extinctions and mass mortality events that suggest a very catastrophic history. Furthermore, the preservation of these faunas/floras requires rapid burial for fossilization. The majority of the sediments containing these remains have been laid down by water under high rates of sedimentation. Many of these events involved massive inundation processes and could have been affected by volcanic eruptions, as indicated by the volcanic ash present in many of these sedimentary deposits.

Currently, these events are accepted by mainstream scientists in the context of a paradigm known as "the new catastrophism." This approach holds that numerous catastrophes punctuated the period of Phanerozoic sedimentation, conventionally believed to span approximately 540 million years, with long time lapses with little or no significant catastrophic events in between. An alternative view proposes that there is little evidence for the lapse of time proposed between extinctions and mass mortalities, constraining time for the fossil record to relatively shorter periods of time. A worldview that considers a short timescale for the Phanerozoic would therefore give more emphasis to the catastrophic nature of the geologic record.

It has been suggested[8] that the Designer created the universe and the earth for observation and discovery. Discovery requires the gathering of data, and it is gratifying that abundant data have been collected which provide greater confidence in the Designer's revealed biblical record of Earth's history. Although there is still much to learn and understand, my faith is affirmed by discovering that the biblical account of mass mortality and catastrophic activity during a global Flood finds resonance with a clear signal of catastrophe and extinction in the fossil record.

PART IX

Vestiges of Catastrophe

42

Turbidity Currents:
Moving Sediment Fast and Far

Ronny Nalin

If you have ever played with sand on a beach you know what a sedimentary deposit is: an accumulation of particles (also known as grains or clasts) of variable size, resting at the end of a journey of erosion and transport. When hardened and cemented, the deposit earns the title of sedimentary rock. The surface of the earth is littered with such rocks, often forming piles that can be several kilometers thick. Since the beginning of modern geology, two differing schools of thought have been in contention about the dominant pathway responsible for these accumulations of sediment. One, the "inch by inch" school,[1] stresses the importance of a gradual buildup of sediment over time. The other, the "catastrophist" school, posits that much of what is preserved in the sedimentary record formed during rapid, episodic events, rising above the level of background sedimentary noise.[2]

The catastrophist approach is of obvious appeal for a person holding a worldview that embraces a recent creation and a historical global Flood. However, its viability requires physical mechanisms able to transport large volumes of sediment over long distances in relatively short amounts of time. Perhaps one of the most exciting breakthroughs in sedimentology that continues to unfold to this day was the recognition of the importance of one such mechanism: sediment gravity flows, and turbidity currents in particular.

Sediment gravity flows are mixtures of fluid and sediment kept in motion by gravitational energy along a sloping surface. Depending on the properties of the fluid and sediment, different flows can develop, eventually producing beds with distinctive and predictable internal organization and physical structures. Turbidity currents are one type of these flows, driven by a density contrast between sediment-laden fluid and ambient fluid, with grains kept in suspension by turbulence. The resulting deposits, called "turbidites," typically consist of graded beds with a lower sandy partition overlain by a finer-grained partition.

The identification of turbidity currents as a major mechanism for the generation of graded bedding took place in the 1950s and represented a true revolution for sedimentary geology.[3] Up to that time, it had proven difficult to account for the origin of some thick sedimentary successions consisting of regularly interbedded sandstone and mudstone. Sands were perceived as a type of sediment restricted to shallow waters, and their tight association and alternation with mudstones bearing the signatures of deep water deposition was puzzling.[4] The turbidity current model effectively solved this enigma, providing a physical process capable of transporting sediment stored on the continental platforms all the way to abyssal depths. It also explained why coarser and finer particles were separated in turbidite bedding: they traveled at different depths within the same sediment plume and were selectively deposited at different times during the waning of the flow.

Technological advancements in oceanographic research are contributing much data that increase our understanding of turbidity currents. Notably, modern oceanic turbidity currents in continental margins have been "caught in the act," with direct documentation of flow velocities of several meters per second, movement at the base of the flow of large objects weighing several hundred kilograms, and run-off distances of tens of kilometers.[5] Another relatively recent development includes recognition of a linkage between sustained fluvial discharge of sediment during river flooding events and initiation of submarine density gravity flows, directly integrating fluvial and deltaic systems with deep basinal deposits.[6] Finally, many mudstone units (and the finest-grained partition of turbidites), previously thought to represent settling from suspension in quiet waters, are being reinterpreted as forming under flowing currents. This makes mud-rich, low-density turbidity currents a likely mechanism for lateral transport of fine sediment, and even lime mud, to deep basinal areas.[7]

Turbidity currents are presently considered to be among the most important agents of transport on the earth.[8] No precise estimates exist on what percentage of sedimentary rocks and deposits consists of turbidites, but they are known to have built massive, kilometer-thick submarine fans, like the Bengal Fan, and represent an important target reservoir rock for hydrocarbon exploration, with examples preserved throughout the geologic column.[9]

If deposition by turbidity currents fits well the catastrophist approach, it is also true that there are other kinds of deposits (e.g., some carbonate buildups) for which I do not currently know a good catastrophist explanation. A certain amount of time between individual turbidity currents is also implied by the common occurrence of trace fossils at the top of turbiditic beds, indicative of the activity of living organisms on the substrate between flows. However, it is not a bad time to be a "catastrophist" geologist. The turbidity current revolution is just one of the examples showing a heightened sensitivity for and renewed recognition of the importance of rapid deposition. Granted, this "neocatastrophism" continues to favor a view of the earth as a system tending toward equilibrium, with occasional disturbances gradually readjusted. However, accepting a short time frame since Creation week does imply a major role for catastrophic processes, providing a firm compass to read the rocks and make a positive contribution in the modern scientific environment.

I find it fascinating that the Bible gives us an extensive account of the Flood, a global catastrophe that affected the earth. Taking this explicit reference seriously could lead us to a point of intersection between the physical and the revealed, where faith is affirmed through history.

43

Megabreccias:
A Record of Catastrophes

Art Chadwick

Many geologic phenomena of the past do not appear to be adequately accounted for in terms of the processes now occurring on the earth's surface. In some cases, it is difficult to conceive of any mechanism capable of explaining them other than through an agency such as the global deluge described in Genesis. Among these problem areas in geology, the explanation of the origin, transportation, and deposition of megabreccias deserves a prominent place.

Megabreccias are sedimentary deposits in which angular fragments of rock in excess of one meter in diameter occur as conspicuous components. A rock equivalent to one cubic meter in volume may weigh three metric tons, and most megabreccia clasts are larger than this. Consequently, transportation of megabreccias to the site of deposition becomes a formidable consideration. Buoyancy supplied by clear water can reduce the weight by one-third or more and can significantly decrease friction as well. As we shall see, conditions in the past enabled rocks of truly enormous dimensions to be moved, sometimes over great distances.

Submarine mass transport is regarded as the most common depositional process that can give rise to megabreccias consisting of very large clasts transported over an often considerable distance. Such mass wasting processes, like submarine slides, slumps, and debris flows, do not necessarily require a steep slope for movement, and there does not appear to be a set limit to the size of clasts that can be moved. The clasts are commonly exotic (blocks derived from a source different from that of the matrix) and are generally supported in a matrix of mud or clay.

A few examples follow from many that could be cited of the results of such catastrophic processes. In Peru, a rock formation covering an area of about 80,000 km^2 contains locally derived blocks of Cretaceous limestone up to one kilometer by several kilometers and up to 500 m thick, and numerous other examples of megaclasts.[1] While it is difficult to pin down a transport distance, at least several kilometers are envisioned. In southern Iran, slabs of exotic rock over a kilometer in size are found in Miocene mudstones, apparently derived from a source many kilometers distant.[2] In the Apennines of central Italy, bodies of transported sediment exceeding 400 m in thickness and covering hundreds of square kilometers of areal extent are known.[3] Many other examples could be added, but perhaps one more will suffice. Wilson reported exotic blocks of Jurassic limestone in Cretaceous radiolarites in Arabia.[4] The largest such block covers an area of 1,600 km^2 and is 1,000 m thick. This and other similar mountainous clasts are postulated to have moved a distance of many tens of kilometers to their present position.

Attempts have been made to develop a non-catastrophic explanation for the presence of exotic blocks in megabreccias. The most common alternative interpretations involve slow tectonic emplacement of allochthonous blocks along thrusts in subduction or collision settings.[5] However, a tectonic origin can be easily discarded for many megabreccia deposits because of the absence of tectonic contacts, presence of wet-sediment deformation structures, stratigraphic attributes indicative of minimal overburden at the time of formation, and spatial changes consistent with depositional trends expected in a basin. An active tectonic regime can still be important as a possible trigger for catastrophic mass wasting, and it has even been suggested that mélanges of tectonic origin can be source units for megabreccias and sedimentary mélanges.[6]

Advances in oceanographic and subsurface imaging are increasingly affirming the importance of catastrophic submarine mass-wasting processes along continental margins and have revealed deposits of a few massive slides containing rafted blocks several hundred meters high and several kilometers in size.[7] However, very little is still known about specific transport mechanisms and triggering forces responsible for the origination and accumulation of megabreccia clasts.[8] It is difficult to imagine forces operative under uniformitarian constraints that would have produced clasts of the size we find in megabreccia deposits.

In conclusion, the presence of various kinds of megabreccias in the geologic record, showing the rapid transport of extremely large clasts over gently dipping or flat substrates for many kilometers, indicates energy levels on a scale that staggers our imagination. Their common occurrence indicates significant catastrophic activity in the past not readily explained in terms of contemporary processes, but consistent with an extended catastrophic episode such as the one described in Genesis.

44

The Colossal Nature of Past Volcanic Activity on Earth

Birgir V. Óskarsson

Evidence of volcanic activity is seen at various levels of the geo-logic column. Examples include lava flows from effusive erup-tions, pyroclastic deposits from explosive eruptions, magmatic veins or bodies that intruded and cooled deeper down in the earth's crust, or reworked volcanic sediments. Volcanic activity today is linked predominantly to two settings: plate tectonic boundaries and mantle anomalies associated with upwelling of hotter mantle material. Con-ventionally, the process of plate tectonics is held to be continuous and relatively uniform; however, the emergence of mantle anomalies is often envisaged as sporadic, rapid, and catastrophic. The source of mantle anomalies is still disputed, but plate tectonics is believed to be the main driver, either triggering shallow mantle upheaval or gener-ating deep mantle plumes from subduction and accumulation of crustal slabs at the core-mantle boundary. Meteorite impacts have also been suggested to create mantle anomalies.

Large Igneous Provinces

The surface expression of mantle anomalies that push through the crust are large volcanic areas. Volcanism associated with these anoma-lies occur both in continental and oceanic settings and may be located within plates (intraplate) or coincide with plate boundaries. The volca-nics include predominantly widespread and voluminous basaltic lava flows but also include some silicic rocks. Massive volcanic areas of this type have been termed Large Igneous Provinces (LIPs),[1] and some of the best known examples include the Deccan traps, Paraná-Etend-eka Basalts, Columbia River Basalts, Siberian traps, North Atlantic Igneous Province, Ontong Java Plateau, and Karoo Basalts.

LIPs are found throughout the entire geological record. Although difficult to assess because of preservational bias, activity appears to have been high in the Precambrian, with production of rare primitive magmas as komatiites, often interpreted as associated with a stage when the earth was hotter. Also within the Precambrian, we find gigantic dike swarms thousands of kilometers long, such as the Mackenzie dike swarm in Canada, that testify of volcanic events on scales of continental proportions. A few LIPs can be found in the lower Paleozoic, but LIPs are abundant again in the Mesozoic rock record, with massive outpourings of lava in every continent. Although less common in Cenozoic rocks, a few LIPs of significant size formed in the Neogene. This stratigraphic distribution can be ascertained independently from the time frame adopted for the formation of the geologic column.

Flood Basalt Volcanism

Early researchers were quick to realize that volcanism in LIPs represented eruptions of much larger scale than modern activity has produced. In fact, this volcanism was conventionally termed "flood basalt volcanism" because it gave the appearance of "flooding events" in lava terms. The lava flows covered hundreds of thousands of square kilometers with volumes of thousands of cubic kilometers, whereas modern activity has formed flow fields in the range of tens of square kilometers and volumes usually much less than 10 km^3. One of the smallest LIPs but the best studied, the Columbia River Basalt Group in the northwestern United States, includes individual lava fields with estimated areas of more than 40,000 km^2 and flows with volumes in excess of 2,000 km^3.[2] One of the largest fissure eruptions in modern times, the Laki eruption of Iceland in 1783–1784, formed a lava field of about 600 km^2 with volume of 15 km^3, which is dwarfed by these lava flows in flood basalt provinces.

Flood basalts can be clearly differentiated from modern lava flows by their numerous extensive sheet flows, which are kilometers in length and relatively thick and flat, forming what are called "tabular flows" or "simple flows."[3] A great number of extensive sheets in a particular lava field suggests events with high effusion rates, which is the amount of lava erupted at a given time, and calculations for eruptions forming flood basalts have ranged in the order of 10,000 to 10,000,000 m^3 per second. For comparison, the Amazon River has average flow rates of about 200,000 m^3 per second. Modern lava flows, on the other hand, are composed of numerous lava lobes of varying sizes and shapes, usually only decimeters to meters thick and tens to hundreds of meters long, that reflect much smaller eruptions on the order of 10 to 1,000 m^3 per second.

To better understand the relationship between the architecture of the flows and their effusion rates, imagine opening the water tap lightly: the flux of water is low, and water will flow gently, controlled by the micro topography, and form separate little streams. As you open the tap further, water flux increases and begins to form larger sheets. Similarly, lava flows can form lava fields with numerous small units or lobes at low rates of effusion, while the size of the lava flows gradually increases to form large continuous sheets as effusion rates increase until the entire area is flooded, corresponding to what we see in flood basalts. Lava flows can also thicken as they pond, channelize, or inflate during emplacement, and some flows in flood basalt areas reach over 100 m of thickness this way, which are extraordinary thicknesses for lava flows.

Implications for Models of Origins

The colossal nature of the volcanism associated with LIPs is unambiguous. Recent studies are beginning to link the mantle turmoil and volcanism that form LIPs with other major geological phenomena such as mass extinctions, the breakup of continents, and even the frequency of magnetic reversals. Long-held uniformitarian presuppositions are being replaced with catastrophic models, interestingly shifting the geological thinking back toward a catastrophic paradigm. Careful examination of the tectono-magmatic origin, timing, and synergic effects of this past volcanism is encouraged for proper reconstruction of Earth's past history to account for colossal magmatism of this type.

45

Worldwide Occurrence of Persistent Sedimentary Layers

Raúl Esperante

Most individual depositional events in modern environments are episodic and spatially restricted, resulting in low net rates of sedimentation. This means that present sediments tend to accumulate laterally rather than vertically, often having the shape of small "tongues" or fans that build sideways instead of forming distinct layers upon layers traceable over a wide area.[1] Massive carbonate rocks also compose a significant portion of the sedimentary record, including limestone deposited in ancient shallow water environments over the continents. At the present, carbonate rocks form mostly on relatively narrow continental shelves and deeper marine basins. Some geologists believe that this is a serious problem for the interpretation of ancient sedimentary layers because, in many parts of the world, major portions of the sedimentary record consist of widespread laterally continuous units. I will discuss a few remarkable examples here.

The so-called "Germanic" Trias is a succession of layers capped by the red sandstone beds of the Buntsandstein, interpreted as deposited in continental areas during the Triassic. This succession of layers was first defined in Germany and extends throughout much of central and northern Europe, under the Baltic Sea, England, the Alps, and eastward into Bulgaria. I have seen it in outcrops of significant extension in Spain.

Similar Trias rocks also occur in the High Atlas of Morocco. Equivalent Triassic rocks crop out in large areas of the eastern seaboard of the United States, and, to the West, they are represented by the Moenkopi Formation and the red beds of the Chinle Formation of Arizona, Utah, and Colorado. The layers of the Chinle Formation have a characteristic reddish color and are interpreted as being the result of deposition in channels and floodplains of a large river system. In Mexico, Triassic red beds occur in the Sierra Madre Oriental. In Bolivia and Argentina, Triassic red sandstone beds are interpreted as deposited in fluviatile and alluvial environments, extending over hundreds of thousands of square kilometers on the South American continent.

Another example of widespread deposition are the massive fossiliferous Cretaceous limestones commonly called the "Urgonian facies." In the Iberian Peninsula, these limestones are found along the coast of southern Portugal, in east-central Spain, and in the Basque region in the north. They form spectacular cliffs south of Marseille, cap the Jura Mountains in the east of France and west of Switzerland, and are exposed in the eastern Carpathians, in the Balkan Mountains, in the Crimea Peninsula, and in the Caucasus Range. Comparable limestones are seen in northern Africa, from southern Morocco to southern Tunisia, and I have seen similar rock layers just south of Monterrey, Mexico. This geographic distribution portrays a massive limestone that developed over a wide area more or less synchronously in the past.

The Jurassic Tithonian limestones extend over much of the same territory as the overlying "Urgonian" limestones. The Upper Cretaceous chalk layers that extend through northern Europe, England, eastern Europe, Turkey, and Egypt, are also found in Australia and the United States. Massive limestones of the Lower Carboniferous occur in the Appalachian Mountains, Arizona, the Canadian Rockies and Alaska, western Europe, India and Pakistan, and Western Australia.

Other widespread rock formations could be mentioned here that characterize a significant section of the geological column on our planet. The picture emerging from these examples is one of geographical persistence in rock lithologies. However, alongside this remarkable extension of rock lithologies there is also paleontological persistence: fossils found in those widespread layers tend to be similar across provinces, regions, and even continents. Groups of organisms appear abruptly, not gradually, in the fossil record, and many of them with a worldwide distribution.

Several problems arise when trying to explain these extensive layers and the widespread distribution of similar fossils within a standard geological framework of slow deposition over millions of years. First, compared with what we infer from the study of ancient environments, processes of sedimentation in modern marine and terrestrial environments are of much smaller scale, forming only relatively thin layers spread over small areas. This suggests that in the past, sedimentation must have occurred on a much larger scale both in volume and lateral extent. For example, it has been suggested that some layers in the western United States formed from sand transported from the eastern side of the continent[2] by fluvial systems at least 1,200 km wide, which is much wider than the largest fluvial systems in modern times.[3]

Second, most of the ancient layers show flat surfaces of contact without much evidence of erosion in between. This suggests that sedimentation must have occurred much faster than in the present, as layer upon layer accumulated with minimal time in between to allow for erosion.

Third, as indicated earlier, fossils in these widespread layers show a persistent occurrence across regions and even continents. For example, Eocene limestone rocks containing fossils of nummulites (small, one-celled organisms with a chambered shell) occur in Tunisia, offshore Lybia, Egypt, northern Italy, the Pyrenees, the Carpathians, southern Turkey, Pakistan, India, southwest Africa and Madagascar, Venezuela, Brazil, Mexico, Cuba, and other regions of the Americas. Not only is the distribution wide, but the density of nummulites in the rocks is usually extremely high (geologists call these layers "nummulite banks"), much more than expected from "normal" accumulation in modern environments.

Fourth, preservation of fossils in these persistent layers is commonly very good or excellent, something not expected when burial of biological remains is slow. The excellent degree of preservation of fossils points to rapid burial, often associated with mass burial as well.

In conclusion, a large portion of the sedimentary record consists of widespread layers that cover hundreds of thousands of square kilometers with similar lithologic and paleontological characteristics over several continents. These features are better interpreted in a model that invokes large-scale, catastrophic deposition rather than steady, slow accumulation over millions of years.

46

Widespread Deposits: Evidence Consistent with the Biblical Flood

M. Elaine Graham-Kennedy

The geological record is filled with fascinating data, but it does not tell us how to interpret them. Therefore, a group of geologists can look at the same data and draw different conclusions based on their various areas of expertise, perspective, and bias. Researchers work with tools and techniques to minimize or, hopefully, eliminate bias. Publishing allows others to review, evaluate, and discuss the results of work by various researchers, and multidisciplinary projects also enhance the overall understanding of data. Scientists rely on their objectivity to mitigate the impact of their perspective, and for the most part, their dedication to this principle serves them well.

Since the spring of 1970, when I began formal study of the earth and its history, my bias has been to understand the geologic record from the perspective of a global catastrophe: the biblical Flood. We are told in Genesis that this event lasted a little over a year, but what delighted me in my studies were the multiple aspects of that Flood's activity that I could see in the geological record today. The Genesis account describes a series of sequential events that occurred during that year, such as the breaking of the earth's crust, erosion beginning during the first 40 days during the heavy rains, the waxing and waning of the waters continuing the depositional/erosional processes, then culminating with the drying period of the great wind. After nearly 50 years of living in the world of geology, I still ponder the signature of this global catastrophe in the rock record.

The earth is highly complex, existing in a constant state of flux. It is not possible to duplicate a global catastrophe that lasted more than a year in a laboratory or in nature. Using models, various aspects of the events can be studied. There are multiple models, working hypotheses, results, conclusions, or interpretations that may or may not accurately describe any of the events under study. However, one feature of the geological record stands out to me as a strong indicator of a worldwide process consistent with the Flood: the occurrence of numerous geological units that developed on a global scale.[1] Examples of these widespread deposits include the extensive basal quartzites of the Cambrian,[2] the well-known Devonian Old Red Sandstone, the Carboniferous limestones similar to the Redwall Limestone in the Grand Canyon, and the massive coal beds for which the Carboniferous Period is named. The list could go on, but one distinctive deposit that has grabbed my attention for years is the Permian-Triassic red beds.

B. Waugh summarized their remarkable characteristics when presenting at the 1971 International Permian-Triassic Conference in Calgary, Alberta:

> One of the most remarkable features of the Permian-Triassic is the widespread development of red bed sediments, occurring throughout Western Europe, western, interior and eastern United States, and parts of Russia, China, South America, southern Africa, India, and eastern Australia. Furthermore, the general uniformity of facies types in all such regions must reflect similar tectonic settings of source and depositional area, mode of sedimentation and climate.[3]

Since the descriptions of these deposits in the late 1800s, a variety of mechanisms and climate scenarios have been used to provide interpretations ranging from marine to arid, temperate to equatorial, including nuanced variations based on site-specific data. Whether these deposits are shallow marine, fluvial,[4] eolian, or paleosols,[5] the basic sequence of rocks is consistent. Rusted deposits of clays, silts, and sands are capped by thick beds of gypsum and overlain by limestone. The fact that so many different reconstructions have been offered attests to the complexity of the endeavor of interpreting the rock record. Any interpretation, however, must acknowledge the sheer scale of these deposits, their overall uniformity, and their consistent stratigraphic placement.

The geological record is replete with catastrophes of regional, localized, basinal import, but we also find a clear global depositional signal exemplified by units like the Permian-Triassic red beds. Correlations of similar stratigraphic units across the continents and around the world do not suggest scattered unrelated events but a systematic, planetary-scale process. The globally distributed Permian-Triassic red beds may seem a small part of the geologic record. However, I believe that when considered together with multiple examples of widespread deposits found throughout the rock record, they are consistent with the highly complex, world-cleansing Flood governed by our Creator.

47

Flat Gaps in the Rock Layers Challenge Long Geologic Ages

Ariel A. Roth

We often hear of millions of years being necessary for the formation of the geologic layers of the earth. The long ages proposed are based on a detailed geologic timescale that is accepted as being reliable by much of the scientific community. Most of these layers are sedimentary and are assumed to have accumulated slowly as the result of relatively local activity. This view is in stark contrast to the biblical account of a recent creation and a catastrophic worldwide Flood that would rapidly lay down a major part of the sedimentary record in just one year. Which view is true?

When one examines the sequence of sedimentary layers, one finds major widespread gaps between some of them. In other words, part of the expected geologic layers that are found elsewhere over the earth are missing. Furthermore, the contact surfaces where gaps are located are notoriously flat; layers above the gap lie flat over flat layers below the gap. Geologists use the term "paraconformity" to designate these "flat gaps." They associate the gap in the rock layers to a time gap, representing the time assumed for the formation of the missing layers. However, the fact that these gaps are so flat challenges the proposed long geological ages.

Figure 47-1 gives three examples of paraconformities seen in the sedimentary layers of the famous Grand Canyon of the Colorado River. The three arrows point to lines representing gaps of 6, 14, and 100 million years of missing layers, according to the standard geologic timescale. Both the Ordovician and Silurian geologic periods are missing at

FIGURE 47-1.   View of the Grand Canyon of the Colorado River. Note how flat the layers are, especially at the flat gaps pointed out by the arrows. Also, note in contrast the irregular topography left by the erosion of the Grand Canyon. "My" = million years.

the 100-million-year gap. The gaps are usually assumed to be there because these regions were, for some time, elevated areas. There, sediments would not accumulate, but would instead be weathered, eroded, and transported by streams and rivers to accumulate in lower regions.

However, the expected erosional activity of streams and rivers over the proposed millions of years is not there. Erosion tends to leave an irregular topography as streams and rivers cut deeper and deeper. How much erosion would be expected over the proposed millions of years? An average of 12 studies estimating the present downward rate of erosion of the world continents indicates it is around 60 m per million years.[1] That may seem slow, but it is a rate that would erode our present continents to sea level at least a hundred times over their proposed geologic age.

At that same rate, you would expect ~360 m, ~840 m, and ~6 km of erosion at the three gaps identified in Figure 47-1 for the Grand Canyon. In perspective, the Grand Canyon is only ~1.6 km deep. However, the gaps are still flat, as though little time had occurred between the layer below and above the gap, as is expected for the rapid activity of the great Genesis Flood. Some layers, like the layer at the top edge of the Grand Canyon, are harder than others and would erode more slowly than average, while others, like the layers under the 6- and 14-million-year gaps, are soft and would erode faster than average. Locally, there is evidence of small channel erosion at some gaps, as is the case for the lowest arrow in Figure 47-1, but maximum depth of erosion there is only about 0.5% of the overall average erosion expected over the long geologic ages proposed for that gap.[2]

The flat gaps can be huge, covering hundreds of thousands of square kilometers, and are found in many regions of the world.[3] According to standard geologic interpretations, these would represent vast flat areas, but why were they not sculpted and eroded over the alleged many millions of years? If there is a gap, plenty of evidence for prolonged exposure and erosion would be expected. The lack of this evidence in flat paraconformities challenges the assumption that the long geologic ages ever occurred.

48

Principles for Interpreting the Sedimentological Record

Monte Fleming

O ver and over again I have been struck with the extraordinary differences between the processes that formed many geological formations and those that are currently shaping the earth's surface.

The Pisco Formation is a good example. It is a unit of Neogene sediments on the coast of Peru, containing large quantities of volcanic ash and diatoms, famous for its extraordinary abundance of marine fossils and their excellent preservation. While the Pisco is clearly a coastal marine deposit, the characteristics of its deposition are strikingly different from modern coastal deposits, and many distinct lines of evidence point to its extremely rapid deposition.

Based on my experience researching the Pisco Formation and other formations throughout the geologic record, here are a few principles I would suggest for reinterpreting the geologic column in ways that are compatible with catastrophism:

Think big. While studying ancient deposits, we should assume that they were formed in an event that affected a large area. A noteworthy example of the use of this principle is the work Art Chadwick has done on paleocurrents.[1] In my own work in the Pisco Formation, I applied this principle in two ways. The first was to note the striking similarities between the Pisco Formation and the Monterey Formation on the California coast, both formed during the time equivalent to the Miocene Epoch, and observe that the same processes affected both coasts simultaneously. The second was to recognize depositional events up to the scale of meters rather than just millimeters or centimeters.

The scale of depositional events was important, because radiometric dating gives a time of approximately 13 million years for the deposition of the Pisco Formation. One can derive a deposition rate of 49 mm/kyr by dividing the 640 m of the Pisco Formation's deposits by the supposed 13 million years of deposition.[2] If this slow rate is correct, then it is natural to look for depositional events on the millimeter or sub-millimeter scale. My data showed clear evidence of deposition on the meter scale, however, and if I had been convinced of the 49 mm/kyr deposition rate, I might have missed clear data pointing to much faster deposition.

Do not expect or insert erosion or deposition where none is apparent. Ariel Roth's work on paraconformities, or "flat gaps" as he calls them,[3] showed how extraordinarily widespread this phenomenon is in the geologic column, both laterally and vertically. Processes that create extensive flat surfaces are extremely rare in modern depositional environments. The rule is that erosion creates topographic relief, so it should be extremely surprising to find abundant flat depositional hiatuses throughout the geologic column that supposedly sat exposed to the elements for millions of years without, in many cases, the slightest hint of topographic relief.

Others have noted that the problem of gaps is systematically exacerbated as one studies older and older rocks. Sadler, for example, states that "As the time span of measurement lengthens, longer hiatuses tend to be incorporated into the estimated [sedimentation] rate."[4] This principle also applies on small scales. Again, the Pisco Formation is a good example. There are many evidences of rapid deposition in the Pisco Formation. At one research location, I found evidence of several meters of sediment being deposited in less time than it takes for whale flesh to decay, and numerous studies have shown that the fossils in the Pisco Formation were buried very quickly.[5] Thirteen million years must leave a mark somehow, and we simply do not see that mark in the Pisco Formation.

Pay close attention to data that falsifies long ages. Coastal erosion rates are a good example. Even using conservative measurements of coastal erosion, the continents would have been consumed by the ocean many times over in their supposed history of at least four billion years. Basinal erosion rates tell a similar story—we can measure the sediment that rivers and streams carry to the ocean and use it to calculate the erosion rate of the continent. Even without the help of coastal erosion, basinal erosion would have carried the continents to the ocean grain by grain many times over. One might counter that the continents are renewed from beneath, but this cannot be the answer to the problem created by assuming long ages because a significant volume of old sediments is still present on the continents.

Pay close attention to anomalies in general—if they are real and persistent, they may point to a better model. As we have learned more about the geological history of the earth, it has become clear that the past was very different than the present. In the present, depositional processes on the continents tend to operate on relatively small scales. In the past, it was common for depositional processes to affect entire continents. In the present, local catastrophic events may leave small marks on the topography of the earth. In the past, events of extraordinary magnitude rocked vast portions of the globe. In the present, sediment is usually deposited slowly and quickly churned up by burrowing organisms and other processes. In the past, vast quantities of sediment were deposited extremely rapidly, and only rarely do we see complete bioturbation in ancient sediments.

As a general rule, the ability of modern analogues to fully explain the depositional record breaks down in older deposits.[6] While we recognize many facies and sedimentary structures that are still being deposited today, many Mesozoic and Paleozoic deposits cover such vast areas and evidence such violent depositional conditions that we should apply concepts developed from modern analogues with extreme caution. Nevertheless, we should assume uniformity of law—that is, the laws of nature governing the dynamics of the deposition of the sedimentological record have not changed. If we assume uniformity of law, we are not without tools in piecing together the events of the earth's greatest catastrophe to date and the many smaller catastrophes that followed.

49

Respecting God's Word, God's World, and People in God's Image

Ben Clausen

My research studies plate tectonics horizontally, the geologic column vertically, and radiometric dating measurements of time. This research finds catastrophes throughout the geologic record, but no working scientific model to fit them within a short time frame. In contrast, Exodus 20:11 indicates that God is the Creator of everything and that He did it all in six days. This conflict upsets many people and no solution is readily available. Following is the resulting approach of someone who believes, not because most questions have been answered, but despite many questions remaining unanswered, which is the example the Bible often presents.[1]

Learn from history. Many founding fathers of science were Christians and studied nature to glorify God. Modern science developed within a Judeo-Christian culture where (1) God is a personal God. Since nature is not god, it can be studied without fear. (2) God is a God of law and order, so His creation follows cause/effect relations. (3) God created and pronounced it good, so the creation is worthy of our study. (4) God was free to create otherwise, so nature is known by observation, not just appeal to reason or philosophy or authority. This is the perspective from which I do science.

Know the issue. If God is all good and all powerful, why is there evil? I agree with Charles Darwin in his May 22, 1860, letter to Asa Gray: "I cannot persuade myself that a beneficent & omnipotent God would have designedly created the *Ichneumonidæ* [wasp] with the express intention of their feeding within the living bodies of

Caterpillars.…" I ask about evil, "How long, O Lord?" (Rev. 6:10) and believe that God wants to get the bad stuff over with as quickly as possible.

Do good science. The church wants global scientific leaders[2] and has been incredibly supportive of the research group that I coordinate. God would want us to do good science. These are the guidelines we use:

- *Work toward a constructive big-picture model* rather than attacking scattered features in existing models. We aim not to alienate, but to learn. Look at all the data. Problems with the current model do not automatically mean our alternative is better.

- *Do the research* to test models against the data from nature, and claim from the data only what it can support. Do not expect science to prove the Bible. We are looking for coherence, but not forcing it.

- *Collaborate within mainstream science* to study the processes governed by natural law. Be slow to invoke God's use of fiat over process. We recognize that God may intrude in unexpected (supernatural, miraculous) ways at times, but that He generally works through His beautiful and well-designed enduring laws.

Study large-scale geology. The Genesis record suggests that our research should include physical processes over all space, varying rates of physical processes over all time, and the substantial effects of water on both. This has resulted in flourishing research on data from the literature and that our research group has collected.[3] We are finding that

- *Geological processes interrelate worldwide.* Horizontally, plate tectonics is the basic cause for much of what happens geologically. Vertically, the geologic column describes the historical flow of events that affects the crust, mantle, and core. Large data analysis is necessary to understand the interdependence of all the parts.

- *Geological rates vary over Earth's history.* Tectonic plate movement changes speed and direction. Magmatic activity forming granites and volcanoes experiences flare-ups and lulls. Magmatic heat flows at different rates by conduction, convection, advection, and radiation. Rates for these processes are affected by fluids. Stable isotopes can help establish fluid sources. Radiogenic isotopes reflect plate tectonic and magmatic processes and sources, as well as age.

Recognize human limitations. Humans are limited in their interpretation of both the Word and the world, meaning that at times reinterpretation is necessary. We know only in part, and even that knowledge will vanish (1 Cor. 13:8–9). God's ways are higher than ours (Isa. 55:8–11). Jesus had many things to say to His disciples, but they were not able to bear them (John 16:12).

Coherence may not be readily available, and apparent paradoxes may easily exist. Physics has the paradox of light being both wave and particle. Theology presents the paradox of God's omniscience and human free will and of Jesus being both divine and human.

Evidence and reason are important, but often more is needed. Jesus stated that He is the truth, not a set of data or arguments (John 14:6). Søren Kierkegaard talks of reason plus a leap of faith.[4] G. K. Chesterton proposes that "you can only find truth with logic if you have already found truth without it."[5] C. S. Lewis suggests in his essay "On Obstinacy in Belief" that it is not an argument that demands your assent, but the personal Christ who demands your confidence, because faith in a theory is proportional to the evidence, but faith in a person is based on experience.[6]

Treat people well. "We draw people to Christ not by loudly discrediting what they believe, by telling them how wrong they are and how right we are, but by showing them a light that is so lovely that they want with all their hearts to know the source of it."[7]

The church leaders in Christ's day wanted a Messiah to conquer the Romans, but Jesus came to conquer the heart. Our research group wants to win hearts more than arguments. We will only be trusted in subjects scientists do not know if we are trusted in subjects they do know. My belief is based on the picture the Bible and nature present of God's character, of a good and powerful God fully existing as Jesus Christ (Col. 1–2).[8]

Recently a geology colleague and I submitted a joint letter to a geology discussion group. The letter stated that we not only communicate about science and religion but also work together. We are good friends who trust and respect each other. We are doing great science funded in part from church sources. His life has been enriched by the kind and thoughtful people in my church. I have become a portal into the church community about science and faith. Together we communicate using the two-book approach.

The research group I coordinate aims to respect God's Word, God's world, and people created in God's image.

50

Human Life Span after the Flood

John F. Ashton

The decline in life span after Noah's Flood as reported in the Bible has been of interest to me for some time for two reasons. First, are there clues in this reported data that would help confirm the scientific and historical accuracy of the Bible, and, second, are there clues that would help us achieve a longer span of quality life today?

At the present time, the typical male life span in developed countries is in the order of 80 years, and an increasing number of people are living to over 100 years with there being an estimated 450,000 centenarians in 2015.[1] However, a study published in *Nature* in 2016 suggests that the maximum human life span likely to be attainable is around 125 years.[2]

Before Noah's Flood, the Bible records that the Patriarchs routinely lived to be around 900 years of age, but after the Flood the life spans had declined to around 120 years by the time of Moses and Joshua. Why did this decline happen? And why is there now an apparent age ceiling of only 125 years?

Recent studies of human aging suggest that longevity is a combination of genetics and lifestyle.[3] From a lifestyle perspective, the recommended diet for the pre-Flood patriarchs was plant based, and they had to grow their own food and walk most places—everything was done manually. So we have the combination of diet and exercise. Now we have growing evidence, popularized by books such as *Forks over Knives* and *The Blue Zone Solution*, that a plant-based diet and exercise are probably the two main lifestyle factors that contribute to longevity that apply today.

Genetics, on the other hand, paints a very different picture. Mutations in genes can adversely affect the maintenance of cells and their basic metabolism and are involved in modulating life span. It is revealing that human mitochondrial DNA is steadily accumulating mutations. In fact, from current estimates of the rates at which the human genome is accumulating mutations, it has been suggested that life on Earth cannot be millions of years old because during that time, mutations producing defects would have accumulated to the point that life could no longer survive.

Dr. J. C. Sanford, who was a genetics researcher at Cornell University, has found that the decline in life span after the Flood is not unlike what would be expected from a genomic decay curve. The high fit of the biblical age records with a scientific prediction provides strong evidence that the ages recorded are historically accurate.[4]

Walter Makous, Professor of Brain and Cognitive Sciences and of Visual Science at the University of Rochester, has critically evaluated the biblical numbers to answer the question of whether or not these biblical ages represent actual longevities or are fabricated. His analysis showed that the "mathematical properties of these numbers favor natural origin. In other words, the biblical longevities as a set are likely to be true."[5]

What then could explain the sudden rapid increase in the rate of genetic mutations after the Flood as suggested by the shape of the declining age curve? A cancer research paper published a few years ago may provide a clue.[6] The researchers reported that when cancer patients were given water that had reduced levels of heavy water (that is, water containing the heavier hydrogen isotope, deuterium), they survived longer. This finding is consistent with observations that when the deuterium content of water is increased, the number of mutations in the cell DNA increases.

Therefore, changes in environmental conditions before and after the Flood, such as heavy water content in the biosphere, are likely to have increased the rate of DNA mutations and reduced life span. Of course, another environmental factor that is likely to have contributed to a reduced life span is the introduction of flesh foods. The original Edenic diet was plant based (Gen. 1:29; 3:18). Then, after the Flood, flesh foods were permitted (Gen. 9:3–4). There is a growing body of evidence that a high-animal-protein diet is associated with reduced life expectancy.[7]

There is substantial evidence from the fossil record that Earth's climate prior to the Flood was quite different to the post-Flood climate seen today. Lush forests covered all of the continents on earth including Antarctica, and land and ocean temperatures were warmer. Carbon dioxide levels were higher and the lush vegetation probably resulted in higher oxygen levels in the air. How the pre-Flood climate affected life span and whether there were other factors affecting life spans in some way such as the strength of the earth's magnetic field and cosmic ray flux are unknown. From what we can study today, accelerated genomic decay after the Flood combined with the introduction of flesh foods provides a reasonable explanation.

What I have discussed in this chapter is just a small snippet of evidence that supports the claim that the Bible is a divinely inspired document and that the health and lifestyle guides contained in it are the best advice for those of us living today.

CONCLUSION

51

A Story of Brokenness, Hope, and Restoration

David N. Mbungu

The book of Genesis begins with a narrative of God as the Creator: "In the beginning God created the heavens and the earth" (Gen. 1:1). Affirming this truth, the psalmist declares: "For he spoke, and it came to be; he commanded, and it stood firm" (Ps. 33:9). The apostle Paul says just as much when he ascribes to God the unique prerogative of giving "life to the dead" and calling "those things which do not exist as though they did" (Rom. 4:17 NKJV). The biblical narrative also states that God created humans "in his own image" (Gen. 1:27), which suggests, among other things, endowment of humans by their Creator with attributes not found in the rest of creation.

At the end of the Creation week, everything God had made was indeed "very good" (Gen. 1:31). Scripture does not tell us how long the original state of perfection lasted before sin entered the world, and with sin came pain, suffering, and death. If we understand design to infer the capacity to fashion material substance from a mental template, it is conceivable that the Omnipotent vested humans with the capacity to think (*design*) and act in order to equip them as co-workers in the plan of the restoration of fallen humanity. The apostle Paul affirms this when he states that "we are co-workers in God's service" (1 Cor. 3:9).

The co-working of God and humans is especially revealed by our capacity to design and fabricate equipment whose medical applications minimize human pain and suffering. Ever since I was diagnosed with end stage renal disease (ESRD, or kidney failure) almost 20 years ago, I have relied heavily on dialysis therapy for survival.

The term "dialysis" refers to the process of separating substances in a liquid based on their ability to pass through a membrane. In a clinical setting, the dialysis procedure purifies blood in patients who have been diagnosed with kidney failure. Two forms of dialysis are currently used in clinical settings. In peritoneal dialysis, a solution (dialysate) is infused into the abdominal cavity for a predetermined time. Through the peritoneal membrane, which lines the abdominal cavity, waste diffuses from the blood into the dialysate and the waste-laden dialysate is periodically replaced with fresh solution as prescribed by the physician. In hemodialysis, a human-made membrane (dialyzer) is used to filter wastes and remove extra fluid from the body.

ESRD ranks high on the list of diseases associated with failure of body organs.[1] The dialysis machine is bulky, but its centerpiece is a small structure referred to as the "dialyzer" and is essentially an artificial kidney. Blood and the dialyzing fluid are funneled into this dialyzer, where the two fluids come very close to each other but flow in opposite directions, a phenomenon referred to as countercurrent flow. This flow arrangement creates a concentration gradient between the two fluids, providing the impetus for the waste to diffuse from blood into the cleaning fluid. The dialysis process occurs along the entire length of the cellophane membrane separating the two fluid chambers and at the end, the clean blood is returned to the body while the waste-laden fluid is drained away.

The artificial kidney has improved the quality of medical care and drastically reduced the mortality associated with ESRD.[2] In the United States alone, over 600,000 people are currently receiving some form of treatment due to ERSD.[3] According to the World Kidney Day website, 8%–10% of the global population suffers from kidney diseases, which now rank high among the major non-communicable diseases.[4] According to the World Health Organization (WHO) bulletin, kidney disease presents risks "across the socioeconomic spectrum from poverty to affluence, from malnutrition to obesity, in agrarian to post-industrial settings, and along the life course from newborns to older people."[5]

The human kidney is a relatively small organ, the size of a human fist. Most people have two of them and they are stuck at the back of the abdominal cavity from where they silently do their job of maintaining constancy of the body's internal environment. The functions they perform include (1) regulating the body's electrolyte levels; (2) maintaining proper fluid volume and blood pressure; (3) signaling the bone marrow to make hemoglobin, which transports gases throughout the body; and (4) regulating the acidity and alkalinity of body fluids.

For both artificial and natural kidneys, solute movement depends on four critical factors: (1) the concentration gradient between the two solutions, (2) the surface area of the dialyzing membrane, (3) the amount of time the two fluids are in close proximity, and (4) the permeability of the dialyzing membrane.

Although it is necessary that human beings be maintained on dialysis following loss of kidney function, human intervention can only go so far. It turns out that the artificial kidney only contributes about 15% of the functions performed by the natural organ. It is therefore no wonder that the health of a patient on dialysis never truly returns to its pre-disease state but is maintained at a new normal. To me, this is a constant reminder that the brokenness we experience in this life will only be healed completely when the Creator makes "everything new" (Rev. 21:5).

A third option available to some ESRD patients involves receiving a donated organ. Transplantation of a donor kidney has the potential to restore body functions to a level sufficient to maintain homeostasis.[6] This enables a longer life with fewer health problems than is possible with those maintained on dialysis therapy. But there is a caveat here too: unless the donor and recipient are identical twins, all other recipients of a transplanted organ have to be on a regimen of immunosuppressant drugs in order to forestall organ rejection.

As I reflect on my experience as a patient with ESRD, I am encouraged by God's foresight and equipping that has given me extra years to celebrate life. Although there is pain and suffering in this fallen world, there is also beauty and grace, and we need to celebrate this. When the apostle Paul pleaded for release from his suffering, he received a most precious promise: "My grace is sufficient for you, for my power is made perfect in weakness" (2 Cor. 12:9). Pain and suffering may be the lot of humans in their fallen state, but God has already provided sufficient grace and hope of restoration. Like the apostle Paul, we too can "glory in tribulations, knowing that tribulation produces perseverance; and perseverance, character; and character, hope. Now hope does not disappoint, because the love of God has been poured out in our hearts by the Holy Spirit who was given to us" (Rom. 5:3–5 NKJV).

NOTES

1 The Fine-Tuning of the Universe

1. PAM Dirac. A new basis for cosmology. Proceedings of the Royal Society A 1938; 165(921):199–208.

2. PCW Davies. The accidental universe. Cambridge (UK): Cambridge University Press; 1982, pp. 69–70.

3. Ibid., pp. 71–73.

4. MA Shulgin. О причинах и целях [About the reasons and goals]. In: Kuznetsov, editor. Научный Фундамент идеи Творения [Scientific Foundation for Creation]. Moscow: Издательство «Протестант» [Protestant Publishing House]; 1993, pp. 55–73.

5. R Penrose. The emperor's new mind: concerning computers, minds, and the laws of physics. New York: Oxford University Press; 1989, p. 344.

2 Where Does Matter Come From?

1. "Design." Merriam-Webster online, entry 1b [accessed August 25, 2020]. https://www.merriam-webster.com/dictionary/design.

2. The biologist Richard Dawkins expresses this sentiment with clarity: "We really need Darwin's powerful crane to account for the diversity of life on Earth, and especially the persuasive illusion of design." R. Dawkins. The God delusion. Boston (MA): Houghton Mifflin Harcourt; 2006, p. 168; "Biology is the study of complicated things that give the appearance of having been designed for a purpose." R. Dawkins. The blind watchmaker. London (UK): The Folio Society; 2008, p. 1; "The illusion of purpose is so powerful that biologists themselves use the assumption of good design as a working tool." R. Dawkins. River out of Eden: A Darwinian view of life. Science Masters Series: New York; 1995, p. 98.

3. RP Feynman. Quantum electrodynamics. Reading (MA): Benjamin/ Cummings; 1962, p. 111.

4. In order to avoid this problem of momentum conservation, some theoretical physicists have proposed that in the early stages of the big bang, physics as we know it today was not valid. Then when did physics start to be valid? It makes more sense to think physics is valid all the way from the beginning, when God created everything.

5. "Baryogenesis" is the term used by astrophysicists to refer to the mechanism that resulted in matter asymmetry. However, baryogenesis is simply a *hypothetical* process that supposedly occurred just before nucleosynthesis, in an attempt

to explain the imbalance between baryons (matter) and anti-baryons (anti-matter). To propose an untestable process is valid solely in the primeval big bang; at the same time, throwing away a well-tested momentum conservation principle does not seem to be scientifically honest.

3 The Periodic Table and Design

1. R Chang, KA Goldsby. Chemistry. 11th ed. New York: McGraw Hill Education; 2012, p. 6.

2. ND Jespersen, JE Brady, A Hyslop. Chemistry: the molecular nature of matter. 7th ed. Hoboken (NY): Wiley; 2014, pp. 77, 382.

3. VS Poythress. Redeeming science: a God-centered approach. Wheaton (IL): Crossway; 2006, p. 314.

4 The Heavens Declare God's Glory

1. For the number of current exoplanets, see https://exoplanetarchive.ipac. caltech.edu [accessed April 22, 2019].

5 Wonderful Water

1. KY Kondratyev, NI Moskalenko. The role of carbon dioxide and other minor gaseous components and aerosols in the radiation budget. In: JT Houghton, editor. The global climate. New York: Cambridge University Press; 1984, pp. 225–233.

2. Ibid.

3. T Oki, S Kanae. Global hydrological cycles and world water resources. Science 2006; 313(5790):1068–1072. doi:10.1126/science.1128845; R. Schäffer. Hydrochemische Methoden zur geothermalen Erkundung und Charakterisierung von Thermalwässern [PhD dissertation]. Darmstadt (Germany): Technische Universität; 2018, pp. 4–5. http://tuprints.ulb.tu-darmstadt.de/7502/ [accessed June 25, 2020].

4. Ibid.

6 From Chemical Space to Creative Grace

1. J-L Reymond. The chemical space project. Accounts of Chemical Research 2015; 48(3):722–730.

2. P Ball. Navigating chemical space. Chemistry World 2015; 12(10):58–61.

3. M Denton. Children of light—the astonishing properties of sunlight that make us possible. Seattle (WA): Discovery Institute Press; 2018, Chapters 2 and 4.

7 Intelligent Computational Agents Require a Designer

1. S Hawking, L Mlodinow. The grand design. New York: Bantam Books; 2012, p. 179.

2. M Gardner. Mathematical games—the fantastic combinations of John Conway's new solitaire game "Life." Scientific American 1970; 223(Oct):120–123.

3. Ibid.

4. R Kohavi, F Provost. Glossary of terms. Machine Learning 1998; 30(2–3):271–274.

5. M Mitchell. An introduction to genetic algorithms. Cambridge (MA): MIT; 1996.

6. GH Alférez, V Pelechano. Achieving autonomic web service compositions with models at runtime. Computers & Electrical Engineering 2017; 63(Oct):332–352.

8 The Matter of Life

1. AI Oparin. Modern concepts of the origin of life on the earth. Scientia 1978; 113(1–4):7–18.

2. M Polanyi. Life transcending physics and chemistry. Chemical Engineering News 1967; 45(35):54–66.

3. Oparin, op. cit.

4. Oparin, op. cit.

5. JL Bada. How life began on earth: a status report. Earth and Planetary Science Letters 2004; 226(1–2):1–15.

6. EE Stueken, RE Anderson, JS Bowman, WJ Brazelton, J Colangelo-Lillis, AD Goldman, SM Som, JA Baross. Did life originate from a global chemical reactor? Geobiology 2013; 11(2):101–126.

9 Origin of Life

1. JW Schopf, editor. Life's origin: the beginnings of biological evolution. Berkeley (CA): University of California Press; 2002, pp. 88–97.

2. NA Campbell, JB Reece. Biology. London (UK): Pearson Education; 2005, pp. 555–556.

3. AB Hughes, editor. Amino acids, peptides and proteins in organic chemistry. Weinheim (Germany): Wiley-VCH; 2009, p. 18.

4. JM Berg, JLTymoczko, L Stryer. Biochemistry. New York: W.H. Freeman; 2012, pp. 96–98.

5. D Axe. Undeniable: how biology confirms our intuition that life is designed. New York: HarperOne; 2016, p. 81.

10 DNA's Designer Alphabet

1. R Dahm. Discovering DNA: Friedrich Miescher and the early years of nucleic acid research. Human Genetics 2008; 122(6):565–581.

2. R Dawkins. River out of Eden: a Darwinian view of life. New York: Basic Books; 1995, p. 17.

3. E Szathmáry. Why are there four letters in the genetic alphabet? Nature Reviews Genetics 2003; 4(12):995–1001.

4. E Szathmáry. Four letters in the genetic alphabet: a frozen evolutionary optimum? Proceedings of the Royal Society B–Biological Sciences 1991; 245(1313):91–99.

5. S Hoshika, NA Leal, M-J Kim, M-S Kim, NB Karalkar, H-J Kim, AM Bates, NE Watkins Jr., HA SantaLucia, AJ Meyer, et al. Hachimoji DNA and RNA: a genetic system with eight building blocks, Science 2019; 363(6429): 884–887.

6. M Warren. 4 new DNA letters double life's alphabet. Nature 2019; 566:436.

11 DNA: A Magnificent Nanomolecule

1. K Mizoguchi, H Sakamoto. DNA engineering: properties and applications. Singapore: Pan Stanford; 2017, p. 349.

2. S Chen. Length of a human DNA molecule. In: G Elert, editor. The physics factbook, 2006. Available from: http:/hypertextbook.com/facts/1998/StevenChen.shtml [accessed June 24, 2020].

3. Ibid.

4. Ibid.

5. S Levy, G Sutton, PC Ng, L Feuk, AL Halpern, BP Walenz, N Axelrod, J Huang, EF Kirkness, G Denisov, et al. The diploid genome sequence of an individual human. PLoS Biology 2007; 5(10):e254.

6. A Turberfield. DNA as an engineering material. Physics World 2003; 16(3):43.

7. NC Seeman, HF Sleiman. DNA nanotechnology. Nature Reviews Materials 2017; 3(1):17068.

8. Ibid.

9. Ibid.

10. Turberfield, op. cit.

11. J Bohannon. DNA: The ultimate hard drive. Science 2012 (Aug. 16). Available from: https://www.sciencemag.org/news/2012/08/dna-ultimate-hard-drive [accessed June 24, 2020].

12 A Look at the Mirror

1. RS Cahn, C Ingold, V Prelog. Specification of molecular chirality. Ange-

wandte Chemie International Edition 1966; 5(4):385–415.

2. LD Barron. Symmetry and molecular chirality. Chemical Society Reviews 1986; 15:189–223.

3. VA Tverdislov, LV Yakovenko, AA Zhavoronkov. Chirality as a problem of biochemistry. Russian Journal of General Chemistry 2007; 77(11):1994–2005.

4. Ibid.

5. Ibid.

6. Tragically, thousands of babies, whose mothers had taken thalidomide while pregnant, were born with external and internal deformities. See SK Teo, WA Colburn, WG Tracewell, KA Kook, DI Stirling, MS Jaworsky, MA Scheffer, SD Thomas, OL Laskin. Clinical pharmacokinetics of thalidomide. Clinical Pharmacokinets 2004; 43(5):311–327.

7. D Ager. Handbook of chiral chemicals. 2nd ed. Boca Raton (FL): Taylor & Francis; 2005.

8. Barron, op. cit., p. 219.

13 Membrane Asymmetry Points to the Creator

1. D Marquardt, B Geier, G Pabst. Asymmetric lipid membranes: towards more realistic model systems. Membranes 2015; 5(2):180–196. doi:10.3390/membranes5020180.

2. M Darland-Ransom, X Wang, C-L Sun, J Mapes, K Gengyo-Ando, S Mitani, D Xue. Role of C. elegans TAT-1 protein in maintaining plasma membrane phosphatidylserine asymmetry. Science 2008; 320(5875):528–531. doi: 10.1126/science.1155847.

3. B Fadeel, D Xue. The ins and outs of phospholipid asymmetry in the plasma membrane: roles in health and disease. Critical Reviews in Biochemistry and Molecular Biology 2009; 44(5):264–277. doi:10.1080/10409230903193307.

4. JM Berg, JL Tymoczko, L Stryer. Biochemistry. 7th ed. New York: W.H. Freeman; 2012, p. 364.

14 Conserved throughout Creation

1. A Annunziato. DNA packaging: nucleosomes and chromatin. Nature Education 2008; 1(1):26.

2. AD Baxevanis, D Landsman. Histone sequence database: a compilation of highly-conserved nucleoprotein sequences. Nucleic Acids Research 1996; 24(1):245.

3. H Xin, W Yanling, W Hua, W Feilong, J Zhenyu, L Tangliang. Nonsense-mediated mRNA decay: a "nonsense" pathway makes sense in stem cell biology. Nucleic Acids Research 2018; 46(3):1038–1051.

4. A Veraksa, M Del Campo, W McGinnis. Developmental patterning genes and their conserved functions: from model organisms to humans. Molecular Genetics and Metabolism 2000; 69(2):85–100.

5. T Czerny, G Halder, U Kloter, A Souabni, WJ Gehring, M Busslinger. *Twin of eyeless,* a second *Pax-6* gene of *Drosophila,* acts upstream of *eyeless* in the control of eye development. Molecular Cell 1999; 3:297–307.

15 Cholesterol

1. HME Cardwell, JW Cornforth, SR Duff, H Holtermann, R Robinson. Total synthesis of androgenic hormones. Chemistry & Industry 1951; 101:389–390.

2. RB Woodward, F Sondheimer, D Taub, K Heusler, WM McLamore. The total synthesis of steroids. Journal of the American Chemical Society 1952; 74:4223–4251.

3. JD Belani, SD Rychnovsky. A concise synthesis of ent-cholesterol. The Journal of Organic Chemistry 2008; 73(7):2768–2773.

4. Cardwell et al., op. cit.; Woodward et al., op. cit.

5. WD Nes. Biosynthesis of cholesterol and other sterols. Chemical Reviews 2011; 111(10):6423–6451.

16 All Natural Chemistry

1. Intelligent Design and Evolution Awareness Center. Irreducible complexity: the challenge to the Darwinian evolutionary explanations of many biochemical structures, 2004; p. 2. http://www.ideacenter.org/contentmgr/showdetails.php/id/840 [accessed June 15, 2020]; MJ Behe. Darwin's black box: the biochemical challenge to evolution. New York: Free Press; 1996, pp. 39–40.

2. Wikipedia, Photosystem II. https://en.wikipedia.org/wiki/Photosystem_II#:~:text=Photosystem%20II%20(or%2water%2Dplastoquinone,plant%2C%20algae%2C%20and%20cyanobacteria [accessed June 24, 2020].

17 The Signature of the Creator Revealed in Photosynthesis

1. J Whitmarsh, Govindjee. The photosynthetic process. In: GS Singhal, G Renger, SK Sopory, KD Springer, editors. Concepts in photobiology: photosynthesis and photomorphogenesis. New York: Springer; 2013, pp. 11–51.

2. R Muhaidat, RF Sage, NG Dengler. Diversity of Kranz anatomy and biochemistry in C4 eudicots. American Journal of Botany 2007; 94(3):362–381.

3. SN Pandey, BK Sinha. Photosynthesis. Plant Physiology. 4th ed. New Delhi (India): Vikas; 2005, pp. 222–239.

4. JM Berg, L Stryer, JL Tymoczko, GJ Gatto. Biochemistry. 8th ed. New York: W. H. Freeman; 2015.

5. EP Odum, GW Barrett. Fundamentals of ecology. 5th ed. Belmont (CA): Thomson Brooks/Cole; 2005.

18 A God of Law, Order, and Beauty

1. Albert Einstein, quoted in MJ Klein, Thermodynamics in Einstein's universe, Science 1967; 157:509.

2. KE Dorfman, DV Voronine, S Mukamel, MO Scully. Photosynthetic reaction center as a quantum heat engine. Proceedings of the National Academy of Science 2013; 110(8):2746–2751. doi:10.1073/pnas.1212666110.

3. DL Nelson, MM Cox. Lehninger principles of biochemistry. 7th ed. New York: MacMillan; 2017, p. 1.

19 The Unseen Wonder of Coccolithophores

1. PR Bown, JR Young. Calcareous nannofossil biostratigraphy. Dordrecht (The Netherlands): Kluwer Academic; 1998, pp. 1–15.

2. C Sardet. Plankton: wonders of the drifting world. Chicago: University of Chicago Press; 2015, p. 7.

3. PH Raven, RF Evert, SE Eichhorn. Biology of plants. 7th ed. New York: W. H. Freeman; 2005, p. 301.

4. Bown and Young, op. cit.

5. Ibid.

6. HA Armstrong, MD Brasier. Microfossils. 2nd ed. Oxford (UK): Blackwell; 2005, pp. 129–140; Bown and Young, op. cit.

7. Bown and Young, op. cit.

20 Foraging in the Ocean Twilight Zone

1. SL Watwood, PJO Miller, M Johnson, PT Madsen, PL Tyack. Deep-diving foraging behaviour of sperm whales (Physeter microcephalus). Journal of Animal Ecology 2006; 75(3):814–825. doi:10.1111/j.1365-2656.2006.01101.

2. Ibid.; S Hooker. Toothed whales (Odontoceti) diving. In: Wursig B, Thewissen JGM, Kovacs KM, editors. Encyclopedia of marine mammals. 3rd ed. Cambridge (MA): Academic Press; 2018, pp. 1004–1010. doi:10.1016/B978-0-12-804327-1.00261-2.

3. GL Kooyman, PJ Ponganis. Diving physiology. In: Wursig B, Thewissen JGM, Kovacs KM, editors. Encyclopedia of marine mammals. 3rd ed. Cambridge (MA): Academic Press; 2018, pp. 262–267. doi:10.1016/B978-0-12-804327-1.00108-4.

4. PJ Ponganis. Circulatory system. In: Wursig B, Thewissen JGM, Kovacs KM, editors. Encyclopedia of marine mammals. 3rd ed. Cambridge (MA):

Academic Press; 2018, pp. 191–194. doi:10.1016/B978-0-12-804327-1.00091-1.

5. K Evans, MA Hindell, D Thiele. Body fat and condition in sperm whales, Physeter microcephalus, from southern Australian waters. Comparative Biochemistry and Physiology–Part A: Molecular and Integrative Physiology 2003; 134(4):847–862. doi: 10.1016/S1095-6433(03)00045-X.

6. Ponganis, op. cit.

21 Squid

1. GD Jackson, JH Choat. Growth in tropical cephalopods: an analysis based on statolith microstructures. Canadian Journal of Fisheries and Aquatic Sciences 1992; 49:218–228.

2. GD Jackson. Application and future potential of statolith increment analysis in squids and sepioids. Canadian Journal of Fisheries and Aquatic Sciences 1994; 51:2612–2625.

3. GD Jackson, RK O'Dor. Time, space and the ecophysiology of squid growth, life in the fast lane. Vie et Milieu 2001; 51:205–215.

4. GD Jackson, ML Domeier. The effects of an extraordinary El Niño/La Niña event on the size and growth of the squid Loligo opalescens off Southern California. Marine Biology 2003; 142:925–935.

5. Ibid., p. 925.

6. ZA Doubleday, TAA Prowse, A Arkhipkin, GJ Pierce, J Semmens, M Steer, SC Leporati, S Lourenco, A Quetglas, W Sauer, et al. Global proliferation of cephalopods. Current Biology 2016; 26(10):R406–R407.

22 Design in the Water-Salt Physiology of Fishes

1. DH Evans. Teleost fish osmoregulation: what we have learned since August Krogh, Homer Smith, and Ancet Keys. American Journal of Physiology–Regulatory, Integrative and Comparative Physiology 2008; 295:R704–R713.

2. RW Hill, GA Wyse, M Anderson. Animal physiology. 4th ed. Sunderland (MA): Sinauer; 2016, pp. 741–753.

3. AP Salati, A Baghbazadeh, M Soltani, R Peyghan, G Riazi. Effect of different levels of salinity on gill and kidney function in common carp Cyprinus carpio (Pisces: Cyprinidae). Italian Journal of Zoology 2011; 78(3):298–303.

23 Interrelated Design in the Swiftlet

1. MK Tarburton. The breeding biology of two populations of the White-rumped Swiftlet in Fiji and Queensland, with special reference to factors that regulate clutch size in birds [PhD thesis]. [Palmerston North (NZ)]: Massey University; 1987.

2. MK Tarburton. Breeding biology of the White-rumped Swiftlet at Chillagoe. Emu 1988; 88:202–209.

3. MK Tarburton. White-rumped Swiftlet colony size and locations in Samoa. Helictite 2011; 40(2):35–49.

4. MK Tarburton. An unusual nest site for swiftlets. Muruk 1990; 4:66–69.

5. MK Tarburton. The food of the White-rumped Swiftlet Aerodramus spodiopygius in Fiji. Notornis 1986; 33:1–16.

6. MK Tarburton, SR Tarburton. Colony stability of cave-nesting Australian Swiftlets in Queensland: what are the impacts of severe weather events? Australian Field Ornithology 2013; 30:131–151.

7. JJ Videler, EJ Stamhuis, GDE Povel. Leading-edge vortex lifts swifts. Science 2004; 306(5703):1960–1962.

8. P Henningsson, GR Spedding, A Hedenström. Vortex wake and flight kinematics of a swift in cruising flight in a wind tunnel. Journal of Experimental Biology 2008; 211:717–730.

24 Mathematics and Design in the Realm of Bees

1. Cited in CB Boyer, U Merzbach. A history of mathematics. 3rd ed. Hoboken (NJ): Wiley; 2011, p. 142.

2. F Morgan. The hexagonal honeycomb conjecture. Transactions of the American Mathematical Society 1999; 351(5):1753–1763.

3. J Nickel. Mathematics: is God silent? Vallecito (CA): Ross House; 2001.

4. LF Deborah. Hidden mysteries of the honeybee. Maitland (FL): Xulon; 2009.

5. AFI Bajunid, MY Abbas, AH Nawawi. Tessellating "honeycombs." WIT Transactions on Ecology and the Environment 2016; 148(June):141–152. doi:10.2495/RAV110141.

25 Phonotaxis

1. K Schildberger. Temporal selectivity of identified auditory neurons in the cricket brain. Journal of Comparative Physiology A 1984; 155:171–185.

2. J Stout, N Carlson, H Bingol, J Ramseier, M Bronsert, G Atkins. The L3 neuron and an associated prothoracic network are involved in calling song recognition by female crickets. Invertebrate Neuroscience 1997; 3:145–153.

3. L Samuel, A Stumpner, G Atkins, J Stout. Processing of model calling songs by the prothoracic AN2 neurone and phonotaxis are significantly correlated in individual female Gryllus bimaculatus. Physiological Entomology 2013; 38(4):344–354. doi:10.1111/phen.12040.

4. S Schöneich, K Kostarakos, B Hedwig. An auditory feature detection circuit

for sound pattern recognition. Science Advances 2015; 1(8):e1500325.

    5. B Navia, J Stout. Prothoracic processing of models of male calling songs by female crickets: roles in behavior? Hokkaido Neuroethology Workshops, Sapporo (Japan): University of Hokkaido; 2014.

26 Design, Spiders, and "Integrated Wholes"

    1. JA Ballesteros, PP Sharma. A critical appraisal of the placement of Xiphosura (Chelicerata) with account of known sources of phylogenetic error. Systematic Biology 2019; 68(6):896–917. doi:10.1093/sysbio/syz011.

    2. R Foelix. Biology of spiders. 3rd ed. New York: Oxford University Press; 2011, p. 140.

    3. W Nentwig, L Kuhn-Nentwig. Main components of spider venoms. In: W Nentwig, editor. Spider ecophysiology. Berlin Heidelberg: Springer–Verlag; 2013, pp. 191–202.

    4. AM Cooper, DR Nelsen, WK Hayes. 2015. The strategic use of venom by spiders. In: Evolution of venomous animals and their toxins. Dordrecht (The Netherlands): Springer Science+Business Media; 2015, pp. 1–18. doi:10.1007/978-94-007-6727-0_13-1.

    5. JW Krakauer, AA Ghazanfar, A Gomez-Marin, MA MacIver, D Poeppel. Neuroscience needs behavior: correcting a reductionist bias. Neuron 2017; 93(3):480–490.

27 Spider Silk

    1. R Montenegro. A teia de aranha. Ciencia das Origens 2003; 6:1–5.

    2. TA Blackledge, J Peréz-Rigueiro, GR Plaza, B Perea, A Navarro, GV Guinea, M Elices. Sequential origin in the high performance properties of orb spider dragline silk. Scientific Reports 2012; 2:782; KN Savage, JM Gosline. The role of proline in the elastic mechanism of hydrated spider silks. Journal of Experimental Biology 2008; 211(12):1948–1957.

    3. L Eisoldt, A Smith, T Scheibel. Decoding the secrets of spider silk. Materials Today 2011; 14(3):80–86.

    4. JO Wolff, A van der Meijden, ME Herberstein. Distinct spinning patterns gain differentiated loading tolerance of silk thread anchorages in spiders with different ecology. Proceedings of the Royal Society B–Biological Sciences 2017; 284:20171124. doi:10.1098/rspb.2017.1124.

    5. M Cho, P Neubauer, C Fahrenson, I Rechenberg. An observational study of ballooning in large spiders: nanoscale multifibers enable large spiders' soaring flight. PLoS Biology 2018; 16(6):e2004405. doi:10.1371/journal.pbio.2004405.

    6. RJ Challis, SL Goodacre, GM Hewitt. Evolution of spider silks:

Conservation and diversification of C-terminus. Insect Molecular Biology 2006; 15(1):45–56.

7. O Tokareva, M Jacobsen, M Buehler, J Wong, D Kaplan. Structure-function-property-design interplay in biopolymers: spider silk. Acta Biomaterialia 2014; 10(4):1612–1626.

8. PA Selden, JC Gall. A Triassic mygalomorph spider from the northern Vosges, France. Palaeontology 1992; 35:211–235.

28 Extreme Plasticity in the Skull Shape of Dogs

1. AG Drake, CP Klingenberg. Large-scale diversification of skull shape in domestic dogs: disparity and modularity. The American Naturalist 2010; 175(3):289–301. doi:10.1086/650372.

2. AG Drake, CP Klingenberg. The pace of morphological change: historical transformation of skull shape in St Bernard dogs. Proceedings of the Royal Society B–Biological Sciences 2008; 275(1630):71–76.

3. Drake and Klingbert 2010, op. cit.; FA Machado, TMG Zahn, G Marroig. Evolution of morphological integration in the skull of Carnivora (Mammalia): Changes in Canidae lead to increased evolutionary potential of facial traits. Evolution 2018; 72(7):1399–1419. doi:10.1111/evo.13495.

29 Our Spectacular Skeletons

1. A Husain, MA Jeffries. Epigenetics and bone remodeling. Current Osteoporosis Reports 2017; 15:450–458.

2. PJ Marie, M Cohen-Solal. The expanding life and functions of osteogenic cells: from simple bone making cells to multifunctional cells and beyond. Journal of Bone and Mineral Research 2018; 33:199–210.

3. T Ono, T Nakashima. Recent advances in osteoclast biology. Histochemistry and Cell Biology 2018; 149:325–341.

4. Ibid.

5. Ibid.

6. Marie and Cohen-Solal, op. cit.

7. Ibid.

8. K Okamoto, H Takayanagi. Osteoimmunology. Cold Spring Harbor Perspectives in Medicine 2019; 9(1):a031245.

9. Ono and Nakashima, op. cit.

10. L Endo-Munoz, A Cumming, D Rickwood, D Wilson, C Cueva, C Ng, G Strutton, AI Cassady, A Evdokiou, S Sommerville, et al. Loss of osteoclasts contributes to development of osteosarcoma pulmonary metastases. Cancer Research 2010; 70(18):7063–7072.

11. Ono and Nakashima, op. cit.

30 The Amazing Gift of Hearing

1. For a general introduction to human hearing, see C VanPutte, J Regan, A Russo, R Seeley. Seeley's Anatomy & Physiology, 12th ed. New York: McGraw Hill; 2019, pp. 534–548.

2. S Frühholz, W Trost, SA Kotz. The sound of emotions—towards a unifying neural network perspective of affective sound processing. Neuroscience & Biobehavioral Reviews 2016; 68:96–110.

3. T Moser, F Predoehl, A Starr. Review of hair cell synapse defects in sensorineural hearing impairment. Otology & Neurotology 2013; 34(6):995–1004.

31 The Human Eye

1. For a more detailed treatment of the aspects of the human eye discussed in this essay, see D Atchison, G Smith. Optics of the human eye. Oxford (UK): Butterworth-Heinemann; 2000; SH Schwartz. Visual perception—a clinical orientation. 5th ed. New York: McGraw Hill; 2017; CW Oyster. The human eye. Sunderland (MA): Sinauer; 1999.

32 Why Chimpanzees Can't Play Chopin

1. DG Pennington, MF Lai, AD Pelly. Successful replantation of a completely avulsed ear by microvascular anastomosis. Plastic & Reconstructive Surgery 1980; 65:820–823.

2. CC Sherwood, AL Bauernfeind, S Bianchi, MA Raghanti, PR Hof. Human brain evolution writ large and small. Progress in Brain Research 2012; 195:237–254.

3. The null mutation of the gene microcephalin produces a genetic abnormality of small brain size called "microcephaly." Recently in utero infection with the Zika virus has been implicated in causing microcephaly in the fetus, presumably by causing mutation of microcephalin.

4. HN Nguyen, X Qian, H Song, G-l Ming. Neural stem cells attacked by Zika virus. Cell Research 2016; 26:753–754.

5. Although there are claims that chimpanzees and other apes have opposable thumbs and even opposable first toes, their function is for crude but strong grip, an advantage in climbing trees. Chimpanzees may even use crude tools, but their neuroanatomy precludes the precision movements of the human hand.

6. L Mannix. Aussie brain-mapper discovers part of brain that lets you play piano. The Sydney Morning Herald; November 22, 2018, Science. https://www.smh.com.au/national/aussie-brain-mapper-discovers-part-of-brain-that-

lets-you-play-piano-20181122-p50hlm.html [accessed June 25, 2020].

    7. C Goldstein. Baptizing the devil: evolution and the seduction of Christianity. Nampa (ID): Pacific Press; 2017.

33 A Mind for Beauty

    1. S Zeki, L Marini. Three cortical stages of colour processing in the human brain. Brain 1998; 121:1669–1685.

    2. NK Logothetis, DL Sheinberg. Visual object recognition. Annual Review of Neuroscience 1996; 19:577–621.

    3. For example, see M Bourne. The math behind the beauty. Interactive Mathematics. https://www.intmath.com/numbers/math-of-beauty.php [accessed June 25, 2020]. But for a contrasting report, see PM Pallett, S Link, K Lee. New "golden" ratios for facial beauty. Vision Research 2010; 50(2):149. doi:10.1016/j.visres.2009.11.003.

    4. EA Vessel, AI Isik, AM Belfi, JL Stahl, GG Starr. The default-mode network represents aesthetic appeal that generalizes across visual domains. Proceedings of the National Academy of Sciences (USA) 2019; 116(38):19155–19164.

    5. K Semendeferi, E Armstrong, A Schleicher, K Zilles, GW Van Hoesen. Prefrontal cortex in humans and apes: a comparative study of area 10. American Journal of Physical Anthropology 2011; 114:224–241.

34 Designed for Maternal Bonding

    1. BE Morgan, AR Horn, NJ Bergman. Should neonates sleep alone? Biological Psychiatry 2011; 70(9):817–825.

    2. SJ Suomi, FC Van der Horst, R Van der Veer. Rigorous experiments on monkey love: an account of Harry F. Harlow's role in the history of attachment theory. Integrative Psychological and Behavioral Science 2008; 42(4):354–369.

    3. J Chambers. The neurobiology of attachment: from infancy to clinical outcomes. Psychodynamic Psychiatry 2017; 45(4):542–563.

    4. T Sarkar, N Patro, IK Patro. Cumulative multiple early life hits: a potent threat leading to neurological disorders. Brain Research Bulletin 2019; 147:58–68.

    5. Z Duenas, JC Caicedo-Mera, L Torner. Global effects of early life stress on neurons and glial cells. Current Pharmaceutical Design 2017; 23(39):6042–6049.

    6. K Braun, R Antemano, C Helmeke, M Büchner, G Poeggel. Juvenile separation stress induces rapid region- and layer-specific changes in S100ß- and glial fibrillary acidic protein-immunoreactivity in astrocytes of the rodent medial prefrontal cortex. Neuroscience 2009; 160(3):629–638.

    7. Duenas et al., op. cit.

    8. CL Bender, GD Calfa, VA Molina. Astrocyte plasticity induced by

emotional stress: a new partner in psychiatric physiopathology? Progress in Neuro-Psychopharmacology and Biological Psychiatry 2016; 65:68–77.

35 A Tale of Two Enzymes

1. For selected publications stemming from this research, see GT Javor. Searching for the Creator through the study of a bacterium. Christ in the Classroom 1997; 19:129–139. Republished in https://classicapologetics.com/ under "J" [accessed June 25, 2020]; GT Javor. A scientist celebrates creation. Ringold (GA): TEACH Services; 2012; GT Javor. Thiol-sensitive genes of *Escherichia coli*. Journal of Bacteriology 1989; 171:5607–5613; H Zhang, GT Javor. Identification of the ubiD gene on the Escherichia coli chromosome. Journal of Bacteriology 2000; 182:6243–6246; M Gulmezian, KR Hyman, BN Marbois, CF Clarke, GT Javor. The role of UbiX in Escherichia coli coenzyme Q biosynthesis. Archives of Biochemistry and Biophysics 2007; 467:144–153.

36 The Marvel of a Functioning Ecosystem

1. A Abada, E Segev. Multicellular features of phytoplankton. Frontiers in Marine Science 2018; 5:144; doi:10.3389/fmars.2018.00144.

2. N Agarwal, DN Kamra, LC Chsudhary. Rumen microbial ecosystem of domesticated ruminants, AK Puniya, R Singh, DN Kamra, editors. Rumen microbiology: from evolution to revolution, New Delhi (India): Springer Science+Business Media; 2015, pp. 17–30.

3. K Smith, KD McCoy, AJ Macpherson. Use of axenic animals in studying the adaptation of mammals to their commensal intestinal microbiota. Seminars in Immunology 2007; 19(2):59–69.

4. B McClure, F Cruz-García, C Romero. Compatibility and incompatibility in S-RNase-based systems. Annals of Botany 2011; 108(4):647–658.

5. H Lodish, A Berk, SL Zipursky, P Matsudaira, D Baltimore, J Darnell. Molecular cell biology. 4th ed. New York: W.H. Freeman; 2000.

37 Cooperation, Empathy, and Altruism in Nature

1. KJ Park, H Sohn, YR An, DY Moon, SG Choi, DH An. An unusual case of care-giving behavior in wild long-beaked common dolphins (Delphinus capensis) in the East Sea. Marine Mammal Science 2013; 29(4): E508–E514.

2. LA Bates, PC Lee, N Njiraini, JH Poole, K Sayialel, CJ Moss, RW Byrne. Do elephants show empathy? Journal of Consciousness Studies 2008; 15(10–11): 204–225.

3. F de Waal. The age of empathy: nature's lessons for a kinder society. New York: Broadway Books; 2010.

4. T Matsumoto, N Itoh, S Inoue, M Nakamura. An observation of a severely disabled infant chimpanzee in the wild and her interactions with her mother. Primates 2016; 57(1):3–7.

5. IB-A Bartal, J Decety, P Mason. Empathy and pro-social behavior in rats. Science 2011; 334(6061):1427–1430.

6. Quoted in H Wein, Rats show empathy, too, NIH Research Matters, December 19, 2011. https://www.nih.gov/news-events/nih-research-matters/ rats-show-empathy-too [accessed October 10, 2019].

7. FBM de Waal. Putting the altruism back into altruism: the evolution of empathy. Annual Review of Psychology 2008; 59:279–300.

8. P Carzon, F Delfour, K Dudzinski, M Oremus, E Clua. Cross-genus adoptions in delphinids: one example with taxonomic discussion. Ethology 2019; 125(9):669–676; P Izar, MP Verderane, E Visalberghi, EB Ottoni, MG de Oliveira, J Shirley, D Fragaszy. Cross-genus adoption of a marmoset (Callithrix jacchus) by wild capuchin monkeys (Cebus libidinosus): case report. American Journal of Primatology 2006; 68(7):692–700.

38 Epigenetic Inheritance

1. BA Pierce. Genetics—a conceptual approach. 7th ed. New York: W.H. Freeman; 2019.

2. RJ Guliuzza, R Lane. A response to "Does natural selection exist?": creatures' adaptation explained by design-based, organism-driven approach: Part 1. Answers Research Journal 2014; 7:403–420.

3. N Rohner, DF Jarosz, JE Kowalko, M Yoshizawa, WR Jeffery, RL Borowsky, S Lindquist, CJ Tabin. Cryptic variation in morphological evolution: HSP90 as a capacitor for loss of eyes in cavefish. Science 2013; 342 (6164):1372–1375. doi:10.1126 / science.1240276.

4. PR Grant, BR Grant. Unpredictable evolution in a 30-year study of Darwin's finches. Science 2002; 296:707–711.

5. MK Skinner, C Gurerrero-Bosagna, MM Haque, EE Nilsson, JAH Koop, SA Knutie, DH Clayton. Epigenetics and the evolution of Darwin's finches. Genome Biology and Evolution 2014; 6(8);1972–89. doi:10.1093/gbe/evu158.

39 Designed Genetically to Survive Catastrophe

1. K Dorst, K van Overveld. Typologies of Design Practice. In: Meijers AWM, editor. Philosophy of technology and engineering sciences, Amsterdam (The Netherlands): Elsevier 2009; p. 457.

2. R Frankham. Genetics and extinction. Biological Conservation 2005; 126(2):131–140.

3. CD Schlichting. The role of phenotypic plasticity in diversification. In: DeWitt TJ, Scheiner SM, editors. Phenotypic plasticity: functional and conceptual approaches, Oxford (UK): Oxford University Press; 2004, pp. 191–200; AP Moczek. Phenotypic plasticity and diversity in insects. Philosophical Transactions of the Royal Society B–Biological Sciences 2010; 365(1540):593–603.

4. A Varriale. DNA methylation, epigenetics, and evolution in vertebrates: facts and challenges. International Journal of Evolutionary Biology 2014; Article ID 475981.

5. A Boyko, I Kovalchuk. Genome instability and epigenetic modification—heritable responses to environmental stress? Current opinion in plant biology 2011; 14(3):260–266.

40 Adapting to Life after a Catastrophe

1. A Klosin, E Casas, C Hidalgo-Carcedo, T Vavouri, B Lehner. Transgenerational transmission of environmental information in C. elegans. Science 2017; 356(6335):320–323.

2. DM Ruden, MD Garfinkel, L Xiao, X Lu. Epigenetic regulation of trinucleotide repeat expansions and contractions and the "biased embryos" hypothesis for rapid morphological evolution. Current Genomics 2005; 6(3):145–155.

3. CE Paquin, VM Williamson. Temperature effects on the rate of Ty transposition. Science 1984; 226(4670): 53–54.

4. CP Ryan, JC Brownlie, S Whyard. Hsp90 and physiological stress are linked to autonomous transposon mobility and heritable genetic change in nematodes. Genome Biology Evolution 2016; 8(12):3794–3805.

5. Ibid.; YM Cowley, RJ Oakey. Transposable elements re-wire and fine-tune the transcriptome. PLoS Genetics 2013; 9:e1003234.

41 Mass Extinctions in the Fossil Record

1. RA DePalma, J Smit, DA Burnham, K Kuiper, PL Manning, A Oleinik, P Larson, FJ Maurrasse, J Vellekoop, MA Richards, et al. A seismically induced onshore surge deposit at the KPg boundary, North Dakota. Proceedings of the National Academy of Sciences (USA) 2019; 116(17):8190–8199. doi:10.1073/pnas.1817407116.

2. Ibid., pp. 8190, 8197.

3. D Jablonski. Extinctions in the fossil record. Philosophical Transactions of the Royal Society B–Biological Sciences 1994; 344(1307):11–17.

4. DM Raup, JJ Sepkoski. Periodic extinction of families and genera. Science 1986; 231(4740):833–836; A Hallam, PB Wignall. Mass extinctions and their aftermath. New York: Oxford University Press; 1986.

5. MR Rampino, BM Haggerty. Impact crises and mass extinctions: a working hypothesis. Ryder G, Fastovsky DE, Gartner S, editors. The cretaceous-tertiary event and other catastrophes in earth history. Boulder (CO): Geological Society of America Special Paper 1996; 307:11–30.

6. DPG Bond, SE Grasby. On the causes of mass extinctions. Palaeogeography, Palaeoclimatology, Palaeoecology 2017; 478:3–29.

7. Ibid. See their Table 1 for a detailed summary of data and proposed causal mechanisms implicated in ~20 mass extinctions since the Early Cambrian.

8. D Klinghoffer. Richards: "Designed for life, designed for discovery." Evolution News & Science Today, April 22, 2019. https://evolutionnews.org/2019/04/richards-designed-for-life-designed-for-discovery [accessed May 6, 2019].

42 Turbidity Currents

1. NS Haile. The "piddling school" of geology. Nature 1997; 387:650.

2. DV Ager. The nature of the stratigraphical record. London (UK): Mac-Millan; 1981, p. 122.

3. E Mutti, D Bernoulli, F Ricci Lucchi, R Tinterri. Turbidites and turbidity currents from alpine "flysch" to the exploration of continental margins. Sedimentology 2009; 56:267–318.

4. Ibid.

5. CK Paull, PJ Talling, KL Maier, D Parsons, J Xu, DW Caress, R Gwiazda, EM Lundsten, K Anderson, JP Barry, et al. Powerful turbidity currents driven by dense basal layers. Nature Communications 2018; 9(1):4114.

6. Mutti et al., op. cit.

7. LP Birgenheier, SA Moore. Carbonate mud deposited below storm wave base: a critical review. The Sedimentary Record 2018; 16(4):4–10.

8. Paull et al., op. cit.

9. T Nielsen, RD Shew, GS Steffens, JRJ Studlick. Atlas of deep-water outcrops. AAPG Studies in Geology 56. Tulsa (OK): Shell Exploration and Production and American Association of Petroleum Geologists, 2007, p. 504.

43 Megabreccias

1. P Callot, T Sempere, F Odonne, E Robert. Giant submarine collapse of a carbonate platform at the Turonian-Coniacian transition: the Ayabacas Formation, Southern Peru. Basin Research 2008; 20(3):333–357.

2. JP Burg, D Bernoulli, J Smit, A Dolati, A Bahroudi. A giant catastrophic mud-and-debris flow in the Miocene Makran. Terra Nova 2008; 20(3):188–193.

3. CC Lucente, GA Pini. Basin-wide mass-wasting complexes as markers of the Oligo-Miocene foredeep-accretionary wedge evolution in the Northern

Apennines, Italy. Basin Research 2008; 20(1):49–71.

4. HH Wilson. Late cretaceous eugeosynclinal sedimentation, gravity tectonics, and ophiolite emplacement in Oman Mountains, Southeast Arabia. American Association of Petroleum Geologists Bulletin 1969; 53:626–671.

5. MP Searle, GM Graham. "Oman Exotics"—oceanic carbonate build-ups associated with the early stages of continental rifting. Geology 1982; 10(1):43–49.

6. W Cavazza, M Barone. Large-scale sedimentary recycling of tectonic mélange in a forearc setting: the Ionian basin (Oligocene–Quaternary, southern Italy). Geological Society of America Bulletin 2010; 122(11–12):1932–1949.

7. M Vanneste, J Mienert, S Bünz. The Hinlopen Slide: a giant, submarine slope failure on the northern Svalbard margin. Arctic Ocean. Earth and Planetary Science Letters 2006; 245(1–2):373–388.

8. DG Masson, RB Wynn, PJ Talling. Large landslides on passive continental margins: processes, hypotheses and outstanding questions. Mosher DC, Shipp RC, Moscardelli L, Chaytor JD, Baxter CDP, Lee HJ, Urgeles R, editors. Submarine mass movements and their consequences. Advances in Natural and Technological Hazards Research 28, New York: Springer, 2010; pp. 153–165.

44 The Colossal Nature of Past Volcanic Activity on Earth

1. MF Coffin, O Eldholm, JK Cochran, HJ Bokuniewicz, PL Yager. Large igneous provinces. Encyclopedia of Ocean Sciences. 3rd ed. New York: Academic Press; 2019, pp. 337–345; RE Ernst. Large igneous provinces. Cambridge (UK): Cambridge University Press; 2014.

2. SP Reidel, VE Camp, TL Tolan, BS Martin. The Columbia River flood basalt province: stratigraphy, areal extent, volume, and physical volcanology. Geological Society of America Special Paper 2013; 497:1–43.

3. BV Óskarsson, MS Riishuus. The mode of emplacement of Neogene flood basalts in eastern Iceland: facies architecture and structure of simple aphyric basalt groups. Journal of Volcanology and Geothermal Research 2014; 289:170–192.

45 Worldwide Occurrence of Persistent Sedimentary Layers

1. AB Shaw. Time in stratigraphy. New York: McGraw-Hill; 1964. DV Ager. The nature of the stratigraphic record. 3rd ed. New York: Wiley; 1993, p. 95.

2. WR Dickinson, GE Gehrels. U-Pb ages of detrital zircons from Permian and Jurassic aeolian sandstones of the Colorado Plateau, USA: paleogeographic implications. Sedimentary Geology 2003; 163(1–2):29–66.

3. RH Rainbird, NM Rayner, T Hadlari, LM Heaman, A Ielpi, EC Turner, RB MacNaughton. Zircon provenance data record the lateral extent of pancontinental,

early Neoproterozoic rivers and erosional unroofing history of the Grenville orogen. Geological Society of America Bulletin 2017; 129(11–12):1408–1423.

46 Widespread Deposits

1. DV Ager. The nature of the stratigraphical record. London (UK): Macmillan; 1973.

2. SE Peters, RR Gaines. Formation of the "Great Unconformity" as a trigger for the Cambrian Explosion. Nature 2012; 484(7394):363–366.

3. B Waugh. The distribution and formation of Permian-Triassic red beds (abstract). Bulletin of Canadian Petroleum Geology 1971; 19(2):373–374.

4. JJ Smith, BF Platt, GA Ludvigson, RS Sawin, CP Marshall, A Olcott-Marshall. Enigmatic red beds exposed at Point of Rocks, Cimarron National Grassland, Morton County, Kansas: chronostratigraphic constraints from uranium-lead dating of detrital zircons. Kansas Geological Survey, Current Research in Earth Sciences Bulletin 2015; 261:1–16.

5. ND Sheldon. Do red beds indicate paleoclimatic conditions? a Permian case study. Paleogeography, Paleoclimatology, Paleoecology 2005; 228(3–4):305–319.

47 Flat Gaps in the Rock Layers Challenge Long Geologic Ages

1. AA Roth. Origins: linking science and Scriptures. Hagerstown (MD): Review and Herald Publishing Association; 1998, pp. 263–266.

2. For a discussion of eight questions about these gaps, see AA Roth. "Flat gaps" in sedimentary rock layers challenge long geologic ages. Journal of Creation 2009; 23(2):76–81.

3. For more examples, see Discussion 16 on the author's website: www.sciencesandscriptures.com.

48 Principles for Interpreting the Sedimentological Record

1. L Brand, M Wang, A Chadwick. Global database of paleocurrent trends through the Phanerozoic and Precambrian. Scientific Data 2015; 2:150025.

2. L Brand, M Urbina, C Carvajal, T Devries. Stratigraphy of the Miocene/Pliocene Pisco Formation in the Pisco Basin, Peru. Geological Society of America 2003 annual meeting, Seattle, Abstracts with Programs 2003; 35(6):160.

3. AA Roth. "Flat gaps" in sedimentary rock layers challenge long geologic ages. Journal of Creation 2009; 23(2):76–81.

4. P Sadler. The influence of hiatuses on sediment accumulation rates. Geo-Research Forum 1999; 5: p. 15.

5. L Brand, R Esperante, A Chadwick, O Poma Porras, M Alomia. Fossil whale preservation implies high diatom accumulation rate in the Miocene–Pliocene Pisco Formation of Peru. Geology 2004; 32(2):165–168.

6. G Nichols. Challenging orthodoxy: is the present the key to the past? The Sedimentary Record 2017; 15(3):4–9.

49 Respecting God's Word, God's World, and People in God's Image

1. B Clausen. What Adventists have to share with the scientific community. Dialogue 2018; 30(3):10–14. Available from https://dialogue.adventist.org/3065/what-adventists-have-to-share-with-the-scientific-community [accessed June 25, 2020].

2. A McChesney. Adventist schools called to become global scientific leaders. Adventist Review 2014; 191(26): 8–9. Available from: https://www.adventistreview.org/affirming-creation/adventist-schools-called-to-become-global-scientific-leaders [accessed June 25, 2020].

3. See http://bclausen.net/ [accessed June 25, 2020].

4. S Kierkegaard. Kierkegaard's concluding unscientific postscript. Princeton: Princeton University Press; 1944, pp. 15, 90–6, 105, 306, 340, 343.

5. GK Chesterton. The maxims of maxim: Daily News, February 25, 1950. In: D Ahlquist, J Pearce, A Mackey, editors. In defense of sanity: the best essays of GK Chesterton. San Francisco (CA): Ignatius Press; 2011, p. 90. https://books.google.com/books?id=A9IwDwAAQBAJ [accessed January 26, 2021].

6. CS Lewis. On Obstinacy in Belief. In: The world's last night and other essays. New York: Harcourt; 1973, pp. 13–30.

7. M L'Engle. Walking on water: reflections on faith and art. Colorado Springs (CO): WaterBrook; 1980, pp. 140–141.

8. Clausen 2018, op cit.

50 Human Life Span after the Flood

1. R Stepler. World's centenarian population projected to grow eightfold by 2050. FactTank, April 21, 2016. Available from: https://www.pewresearch.org/fact-tank/2016/04/21/worlds-centenarian-population-projected-to-grow-eightfold-by-2050/ [accessed June 25, 2020].

2. X Dong, B Milholland, J Vijg. Evidence for a limit to human lifespan. Nature 2016; 538:257–259. doi:10.1038/nature19793.

3. G Passarino, F De Rango, A Montesanto. Human longevity: genetics or lifestyle? It takes two to tango. Immunity and Ageing 2016; 13:12. doi:10.1186/s12979-016-0066-z.

4. JC Sanford. Genetic entropy & the mystery of the genome. Waterloo

(NY): FMS; 2008.

5. W Makous. Biblical longevities: empirical data or fabricated numbers? Perspectives on Science and Christian Faith 2011; 63(2):129.

6. K Krempels, I Somlyai, Z Gyongyi, I Ember, K Balog, Abonyi, G Somlyai. A retrospective study of survival in breast cancer patients undergoing deuterium depletion in addition to conventional therapies. Journal of Cancer Research & Therapy 2013; 1(8):194–200.

7. DG Le Couteur, S Solon-Biet, D Wahl, VC Cogger, BJ Willcox, DC Willcox, D Raubenheimer, SJ Simpson. New horizons: dietary protein, ageing and the Okinawan ratio. Age Ageing 2016; 45(4):443–447. doi:10.1093/ageing/afw069.

51 A Story of Brokenness, Hope, and Restoration

1. JE Hall. Diuretics, kidney diseases. In: Guyton and Hall textbook of medical physiology. 13th ed. Philadelphia (PA): Elsevier, 2016; pp. 440–441.

2. M Mineshima. Optimal design of dialyzers. In: Kawanishi H, Takemoto Y, editors, Scientific Aspects of Dialysis Therapy: JSDT/ISBP Anniversary Edition, Contributions to Nephrology, Basel: Karger; 2017; 189:204–209. doi:10.1159/000450802.

3. Hall, op. cit.

4. Chronic kidney disease.: https://www.worldkidneyday.org/faqs/chronic-kidney-disease/ [accessed June 25, 2020]; US Dept. of Health and Human Services, National Vital Statistics Report. Washington, DC; 2018. https://www.cdc.gov/nchs/data/nvsr/nvsr67/nvsr67_05.pdf [accessed June 25, 2020].

5. VA Luyckx, M Tonelli, JW Stanifer. The global burden of kidney disease and the sustainable development goals. Bulletin of the World Health Organization 2018; 96(6):414–422D. Published online April 20, 2018. doi:10.2471/BLT.17.206441.

6. Hall, op. cit.

ABOUT THE EDITORS AND AUTHORS

Germán H. Alférez is a professor at the School of Engineering and Technology of Montemorelos University. He is the director of the Institute of Data Science at this institution. He holds a PhD in Computer Science from the Polytechnic University of Valencia. His scientific contributions are published in top journals, book chapters, and proceedings of international conferences. He has worked with universities, organizations, and research groups in four continents. His research contributions have been recognized by the National Council of Science and Technology (CONACYT) of the Government of Mexico.

Rowena R. Antemano is an adjunct professor of biology at Mountain View College in the Philippines. She holds a PhD in Developmental Neurobiology from Otto von Guericke University in Magdeburg. She loves teaching natural science courses, looking at cells through a microscope, writing brain-related articles, and conducting health-related seminars. She currently serves as editor in chief for the book project *Grand Designs*, sponsored by the Southern Asia-Pacific Division of Seventh-day Adventists.

John F. Ashton serves as an adjunct professor in the School of Biosciences and Food Technology at the Royal Melbourne Institute of Technology University. He holds an MSc in Chemistry from the University of Tasmania and a PhD in Epistemology from the University of Newcastle. He has authored over 40 peer-reviewed scientific research papers and 15 books. Dr. Ashton is an elected Fellow of the Royal Australian Chemical Institute and a Fellow of the Australian Institute of Food Science and Technology.

Emilia R. Belia is a postdoctoral research associate at the University of Nebraska-Lincoln. She holds a PhD in Earth Sciences from Loma Linda University. Her expertise is biostratigraphy, specifically through calcareous nannofossil analysis. Her scientific research has been mostly concentrated in the Pisco Basin of west central Peru. Her research findings have been presented at several scientific meetings and published in conference articles and peer-reviewed publications. She is currently working on the study of nannofossils from the Cretaceous/Paleogene mass extinction recovered from the Mentelle Basin (western margin of Australia).

Roberto E. Biaggi is an adjunct professor of geology and paleontology at Loma Linda University. He holds a PhD in Biology with a paleontology emphasis from Loma Linda University. He has written several articles and book chapters on various aspects of the fossil record, with a particular focus on the Green River Basin of Wyoming. He is part of the editorial team for the journal *Enfoques*, a publication of the Universidad Adventista del Plata, and is currently involved in various research projects in Bolivia, Wyoming, and Utah.

Danilo Boskovic is a professor of biochemistry in the School of Medicine at Loma Linda University. He holds an MSc in Pathology and a PhD in Biochemistry from Queen's University at Kingston. He authored and co-authored a number of articles about perinatal and postnatal stressors of the newborn and is currently the principal investigator of a research project on risk factors associated with neonatal intraventricular hemorrhage.

José A. Cardé-Serrano is an associate professor of biology at the Natural Sciences Department of the University of Puerto Rico, Aguadilla's Campus. He holds a PhD in Biology from the University of Puerto Rico, Rio Piedras Campus. He teaches several undergraduate and graduate biology labs and classes, and his research interests include the effects of endocrine-disrupting chemicals in reptiles, fruit flies, and sea urchins, as well as bioremediation with bacteria.

Art Chadwick is a research professor of biology and geology and the director of the Dinosaur Science Museum and Research Center at Southwestern Adventist University. He earned his PhD from the University of Miami, followed by additional work in geology at the University of California, Riverside. His current research efforts include systematic analysis of the geologic column in the Colorado Basin and directing a taphonomic study at one of the largest dinosaur bone beds in the world. He has conducted geological research in Grand

Canyon and Yellowstone National Parks, in Peru on fossil whales, and on global circulation patterns through time. In addition to numerous scientific papers, he has recently co-authored a science textbook titled *Faith, Reason, and Earth History*.

Ben Clausen has worked at the Geoscience Research Institute for more than 30 years, during which he has organized many science/religion meetings. He received an MS in Geology from Loma Linda University and a PhD in Physics from the University of Colorado. His nuclear physics research at many particle accelerators and at the University of Virginia resulted in more than 20 papers. His geochemistry research as an adjunct professor at Loma Linda University has been presented at meetings on six continents and in a number of publications. He has lectured and directed field trips on local geology in dozens of countries around the world.

Noble Donkor is the vice president for academic administration and a professor of biology at Burman University. He has a PhD in Wildlife Ecology and Management from the University of Alberta. He has maintained an active research program in the ecology and physiology of ungulates. His teaching of ecology, vertebrate biology, biogeography, and animal physiology has heightened his interest in the mechanisms and design of animal function.

Noemí Durán is the director of the European Branch Office of the Geoscience Research Institute. Noemí has a PhD in Biology from Loma Linda University, and her area of expertise is animal behavior. She lectures on faith, science, and origins topics, and teaches science and religion classes in several theological seminaries across Europe.

Liliana Endo-Munoz works in the pharmaceutical and healthcare industry, managing the medical affairs, clinical trial, and healthcare/scientific writing portfolios, and is an Honorary Fellow at the University of Queensland, from which she holds a PhD in Medicine. She has published widely in her research fields of virology and oncology in major scientific journals including *Cancer Research*, *BBA Reviews on Cancer*, *British Journal of Cancer*, *Oncotarget*, and *Virology Journal*.

Raúl Esperante is a paleontologist and senior scientist at the Geoscience Research Institute. He holds a PhD from Loma Linda University. He has published numerous articles in peer-reviewed journals and has presented in numerous scientific and theological congresses in the North and South American continents, and in Europe and Australia. He is the principal investigator for research projects on the stratigraphy and paleontology of the Pisco Basin in Peru and on dinosaur footprints in Bolivia. He also specializes in the relationship between religion and science and the controversy of creation versus evolution.

Monte Fleming is a postdoctoral research associate at Loma Linda University, where he also earned a PhD in Earth Science. His publications include "The role of wind in sediment removal from potholes in semiarid environments" in the journal *Geomorphology*. His research projects have included an analysis of the sedimentology of whale burial in the Pisco Formation of Peru, the geomorphology of large rock basins on Rock Window Mesa in Arizona, and applied sedimentology at the University of Minnesota. He is currently conducting flume research at Loma Linda University.

L. James Gibson served as the director of the Geoscience Research Institute (GRI) until he retired in 2020. His PhD is in Biology from Loma Linda University. He co-edited the book *Understanding Creation* and *Entrusted: Christians and Environmental Care* and wrote *Origins*, the companion book for a 2013 series of adult Bible study guides. In retirement he is working on a display on design and catastrophe for the GRI.

Luciano González is director of the Geoscience Research Institute branch office in the Interamerican Division and is a professor of mathematics, physics, and science and religion at Montemorelos University. He holds a PhD in Earth Science from Loma Linda University. His current research focuses on stable isotopes and heat flow in magmatic rocks of the American Cordillera. His educational outreach includes authoring the book *Curso Introductorio de Álgebra Lineal*; writing articles such as *Divine Geometry in Nature*, published in *College and*

University Dialogue; and working on launching the video series *Punto-Geo*, with the goal of diffusion through social media of geology, physics, cosmology, and other sciences from a creationist perspective.

M. Elaine Graham-Kennedy is a retired geologist. She holds a PhD in Geology from the University of Southern California. Her research interests have been focused on rapidly deposited sediments in Patagonia and the United States. She has written a book for children on dinosaurs and several articles on faith and science issues, and is currently working on a geomorphology paper that is in preparation for publication.

Rebecca J. Greer is a criticalist at Veterinary Specialty Services in St. Louis, Missouri. She holds a DVM and MS from the University of Missouri, Columbia, and is a DAVCECC. In addition to performing attending and primary clinician duties, she trains residents and conducts occasional research projects with results published in peer-reviewed journals.

Mart de Groot is both retired director of the Armagh Observatory in Northern Ireland and a retired minister in the Seventh-day Adventist Church. He holds a PhD in Astronomy from the State University of Utrecht. He has contributed to several books and published many articles in astronomical research, including *Observed Evolutionary Changes in the Visual Magnitude of the Luminous Blue Variable P Cygni* (together with H. Lamers), and at the interface of science and religion.

Ryan T. Hayes is a professor of chemistry at Andrews University. He holds a PhD in Chemistry from Northwestern University. He has published papers in the areas of molecular electronics, photoinduced electron transfer, and chemical education. Dr. Hayes currently researches new properties of nanomaterials called dendrimers in addition to exploring the chemical design of life on Earth.

Lucinda Hill Spencer is a professor of biology at Southern Adventist University. She earned her MD and MPH from Loma Linda University. She teaches an origins course for biology majors and contributed to the development of origins curriculum resources,

some of which are available online at www.southern.edu/academics/
academic-sites/faithandscience/Origins-Curriculum-Resources.

Christine Jackson is an associate professor in earth and biological
sciences at Loma Linda University. She holds a PhD in Marine Ecology
from the University of Tasmania. She has published a number of scientific papers and is currently working on the trophic ecology of toothed
whales using biochemical techniques.

George D. Jackson is a professor at the Department of Earth and
Biological Sciences of Loma Linda University. He holds a PhD in
Marine Biology from James Cook University. He has published over
90 scientific journal articles from research conducted in Australia,
New Zealand, Thailand, Falkland Islands (Malvinas), the United
States, Canada, and the Southern Ocean. He has held academic and
research positions in five countries including serving as senior Scien-
tist for the Pacific Ocean Shelf Tracking Project for the decade-long
Census of Marine Life.

George T. Javor is a professor emeritus of the Loma Linda University School of Medicine. After receiving a PhD in Biochemistry from
Columbia University, he did postdoctoral work at Rockefeller University. In his scientific career he investigated the mysteries of heme and
ubiquinone biosyntheses in *Escherichia coli*, publishing several important papers on these topics. He also wrote numerous articles in support
of the biblical story of Creation, one of which, titled "Searching for the
Creator through the Study of a Bacterium," has been incorporated in
the series Classic Works of Apologetics. He also published five books,
the latest being *The Best News Possible: You May Live Forever!*

Delano S. Lewis is an associate professor at Burman University
and holds a PhD degree in Entomology from the University of Florida.
He is an insect systematist who specializes in Lepidoptera (moth/but-
terfly) taxonomy, systematics, phylogenetics, and diversity. He pub-
lishes mainly on insects but has published on Jamaican Iguanas, Indian
Mongoose, and a possible bio-rational pesticide, among other things.

Nicholas Madhiri is currently an associate professor of chemistry at Southwestern Adventist University. He holds a PhD in Physical

Electroanalytical Chemistry from West Virginia University. His research interests are in electrochemistry and alternative sources of energy, including fuel cells, and he has had his work published in several peer-reviewed journals.

Jesson Martin is an associate professor of optometry at Kentucky College of Optometry, University of Pikeville. He holds a PhD in Physics from the National Institute of Technology (Bharathidasan University) in India. He expanded his work as a postdoctoral research associate at Indiana University School of Optometry and at the Eye Institute of the Medical College of Wisconsin. His current research interests are in the prevention of myopia in children using smart devices. Some of his recent research presentations include *Continuous Remote Monitoring Device-Eye Distance and Ambience Light in Children* and *Wavelength Optimization of the Retinal Image Quality*. He serves as a reviewer for the Optical Society of America (OSA) journals and the *Journal of Refractive Surgery*.

Nelson C. Martins is an assistant professor of chemistry at Middle East University, Lebanon. He holds a PhD in Chemistry from the University of the Algarve, having done most of his doctoral work at the University of Liverpool. He also completed two years of post-doctoral research at the State University of Campinas. His research interests are in chiral ligands synthesis and asymmetric catalysis for organic synthesis, subjects on which he has co-authored several peer-reviewed papers in scientific journals. He has contributed his expertise as reviewer for some journals of the Royal Chemical Society.

David N. Mbungu is an associate professor of biology at Andrews University. He holds a PhD in Entomology from the University of California, Riverside. In addition to scientific publications exploring biochemical and physiological properties of animal neural systems, he has published research on how the study of evolution in a general biology course in a Christian college might influence the faith commitments of students, and he has reviewed iconic books in the arena of origins, such as *Why is a Fly Not a Horse?* by Giuseppe Sermonti.

Mitch Menzmer is a professor of chemistry at Southern Adventist University. He holds a PhD in Chemistry from Clarkson University. In addition to interest in origins-related issues, his research interests include kinetics of cyclo-enyl cation formation from acid-catalyzed dehydration and/or protonation of alkyl-substituted small ring alcohols and/or alkenes, development of analytical treatments of kinetic data, and quantitative analysis of small protic molecules using proton nuclear magnetic resonance. Each semester, he directs a number of undergraduate chemistry majors in researching kinetic studies of organic reactions.

Rivelino Montenegro is a scientist and entrepreneur in the biomedical field and founder of many companies in Europe, Canada, and the United States. He holds a degree in Material Science Engineering from the Federal University of Campina Grande and a PhD in Chemistry from the Max Planck Institute of Colloids and Interfaces. He is an expert in nanotechnology, biomimetics, and biomedical engineering. Besides his scientific and business activities, Dr. Montenegro is an author and an internationally sought-after speaker for the apparent controversial discrepancies between Bible and science.

Ronny Nalin is the director of the Geoscience Research Institute and an adjunct professor in the geology program at Loma Linda University. He earned his PhD in Earth Sciences at the University of Padova. His research interests revolve on stratigraphy and sedimentology of shallow marine deposits, with an emphasis on carbonate sedimentary products. His scientific contributions in these areas have been published in several peer-reviewed international journals.

Benjamin Navia is a professor of biology at Andrews University. He earned a PhD in Biology with an emphasis in neurobiology at Loma Linda University. Along with being interested in studying the interface of faith and science, Dr. Navia is also active in investigating the neural basis of auditory behavior in invertebrates. His teaching responsibilities include neurobiology, anatomy and physiology, foundations of biology, and issues in origins and speciation.

David R. Nelsen is an associate professor of biology at Southern Adventist University. He holds a PhD in Biology from Loma Linda University. He has co-authored several scientific articles and book chapters, including "The Strategic Use of Venom by Spiders"; "Venom Collection from Spiders and Snakes: Voluntary and Involuntary Extractions ("Milking") and Venom Gland Extractions"; and "Poisons, Toxungens, and Venoms: Redefining and Classifying Toxic Biological Secretions and the Organisms that Employ Them." His current research focuses on the behavioral ecology of venom and silk use by arachnids.

Birgir V. Óskarsson is a researcher in geology at a governmental institution in Iceland. His field of specialization is volcanology, in which he holds a PhD from the University of Iceland. Besides contributing regularly with research in volcanology, he is currently the director of a photogrammetry lab and works with geological mapping of old and active volcanic areas.

Sven Östring is director of church planting for the NNSW Conference of Seventh-day Adventists, Australia. He holds a PhD in Computer Networking from the University of Canterbury. He has published articles on Big Bang cosmology in the *Journal of the Adventist Theological Society* and missional apologetics in the *Journal of Adventist Mission Studies*. His research interests include comparing warrant in Adventist and scientific epistemology and identifying effective ways of communicating the truth and attractiveness of the Adventist theological system.

David G. Pennington is an emeritus associate professor of plastic and reconstructive surgery at Macquarie University, and he was formerly head of the department of plastic surgery at Royal Prince Alfred Hospital. He currently practices as an expert medico-legal consultant in plastic surgery. He is a medical graduate of the University of Sydney (MBBS) and holds surgical fellowships in the Royal College of Surgeons of Edinburgh and the Royal Australasian College of Surgeons. He was the first person in the world to replant a human ear using the microsurgical technique and is a recognized expert in the field of microsurgical reconstruction. He has fifty peer-reviewed publications in various fields of plastic and reconstructive surgery. He is currently a reviewer for the *Australian Journal of Plastic Surgery* and was a contributor and editor of the textbook *ByDesign Biology*.

Glenn Phillips is an instructional technologist in the North American Division Learning Interactives Department at Loma Linda University and is an academic coach for the chemistry department at Lamar University. He holds a PhD in Synthetic Organic Chemistry from Michigan State University. He has written two books of lecture notes in organic chemistry based on his former experience as professor of chemistry at Oakwood University and the University of South Alabama. He is currently working as the subject matter expert for a project titled "Reactions: Chemistry Lab Simulations."

Aleksei Popov is a specialist in elementary particle physics who holds the position of senior scientist at the Institute for High Energy Physics (Protvino, Russia), where he also earned his PhD in Physics. During his career, he has participated in several successful physics experiments at his own Institute, at Brookhaven National Laboratory, and at Fermi National Accelerator Laboratory. He has authored and co-authored numerous scientific publications.

Humberto M. Rasi holds a PhD in Hispanic Literature and Latin American History from Stanford University, with postdoctoral work at Johns Hopkins University. He served as faculty and graduate dean at Andrews University, as vice-president for editorial development at Pacific Press, and as Education Department director for the General Conference of Seventh-day Adventists. Rasi has published many articles and coedited several books, including *Understanding Creation: Answers to Questions on Faith and Science*; *Always Prepared: Answers to Questions about Our Faith*; and *Entrusted: Christians and Environmental Care*. He launched the journal *College and University Dialogue*, and he directs the Adventus21 Editorial Consortium.

Ariel A. Roth is retired director of the Geoscience Research Institute. He holds a PhD in Biology from the University of Michigan. He has served as faculty at Andrews University and Loma Linda

University and has been studying the controversy between science and the Bible for some 70 years. His publications include some 200 articles in the scientific and popular press, and two books available in 17 and 24 languages. His webpage is www.sciencesandscriptures.com.

Wellington dos Santos Silva is a retired professor of human genetics and science and religion at the Bahia Adventist College. He earned a PhD in Human Genetics from the University of Brasília and a postdoctoral degree from the medicine and health program at the Federal University of Bahia. His main area of research is sickle cell disease in Afro-descendant populations in the State of Bahia, Brazil, a subject on which he has published several peer-reviewed articles. After his retirement, he continues to be involved in the creationist community in his country.

Rafael Schäffer works as postdoctoral scientist and lecturer at the Technical University of Darmstadt, where he also earned his PhD in Geosciences. His research areas are geothermal, thermal, and mineral groundwaters, hydrochemistry, as well as alpine hydrogeology. He enjoys giving popular scientific talks on science and faith and on creation and evolution.

Warren A. Shipton is a past president of Asia-Pacific International University, Thailand, and was designated as professor, in perpetuity, by the Thai Palace and Government, being the first foreigner to be so recognized. He holds a PhD in Agricultural Science from the University of Sydney and a MEd from James Cook University. He has written/co-authored nine books, has published extensively in professional journals on microbiology, and has written on a variety of subjects in other journals and magazines. In retirement, he is an associate editor for the journal *Human Behavior, Development, and Society*.

Tiago A. J. de Souza is professor of science and religion and genetics/evolution at the Centro Universitário Adventista de São Paulo, and he is an invited lecturer at the Department of Biology at Andrews University. He earned his PhD in Genetics at the University of São Paulo. He has expertise in cytogenetics, molecular genetics, nanotoxicology, and evolution; has authored articles and book chapters on these subjects; and is a peer reviewer for leading academic journals.

Alfredo Takashi Suzuki is an associate professor of physics at La Sierra University. He holds a PhD in Physics from the University of London. His current research interests are in the areas of relativistic quantum field dynamics in the light-front and also in negative dimensional integration method in quantum field theories. In addition to publishing several research articles on these subjects, he has co-authored a high school physics textbook, a popular-level book on origins, and a research book titled *Boson Propagators on the Light-Front.*

Michael Tarburton is retired dean of the School of Science and Technology at Pacific Adventist University. He holds a professorship from that university and a PhD in Zoology from Massey University. He has published one book and 64 research papers as well as co-authored seven papers, mostly on swifts, but also on other birds and one mammal. Currently he is involved in research on swifts, swiftlets, and Tawny Frogmouths as well as maintaining three webpages: www.swiftsoftheworld.info, www.evidenceforevolution.info, and www.birdsofmelanesia.net.

Susan Thomas is dean of Sciences at Spicer Adventist University. She holds a PhD in Botany from the University of Pune, India. She has taught philosophy of science classes at both the undergraduate and graduate levels and is engaged in a number of creation-evolution discussions and presentations. She guides students in research with focus on applications in biotechnology, mycology, medicinal plants, and nanotechnology.

Elena Titova works at the Belarusian Republican Foundation for Fundamental Research, which provides support for research on a competitive basis. She earned her PhD at the Institute of Photobiology of the Belarusian Academy of Sciences. She has authored many scientific articles on the metabolic characteristics of a photosynthetic apparatus and has written two books on the subject of Creation.

John C. Walton is a research professor of chemistry at the University of St. Andrews. He holds a DSc in Chemistry from the University of Sheffield and is a Fellow of the Royal Society of Edinburgh, Scotland's National Academy. He has published over 300 articles in learned journals as well as three books. He is currently writing a book on compact time.

Carrie A. C. Wolfe is a professor of chemistry at Union College (Lincoln, NE). She holds a PhD in Chemistry from the University of Nebraska-Lincoln. In her teaching career, she has developed curricular material on the subject of faith and science for courses on origins.

Orlex B. Yllano is the current chair of the biology department at the Adventist University of the Philippines. He finished his PhD in Molecular Biology and Biotechnology at the University of the Philippines, Los Baños. Currently, he is the president of the Philippine Society of Biochemistry and Molecular Biology, South Luzon chapter. He has published papers on conservation genetics, crop biotechnology, and phytoremediation.